GREAT EVENTS
IN THE LIFE OF
FLORENCE NIGHTINGALE

★5 *Is made Superintendent*
of a hospital in London, 1853

★6 *Leaves for the Crimean War*
with thirty-eight nurses, 1854

★7 *Improves conditions in army hospitals,*
saving thousands of lives, 1854

THE STORY OF
Florence Nightingale

"When all the medical officers have retired for the night, and silence and darkness have settled down upon those miles of prostrate sick, she may be observed alone, with a little lamp in her hand, making her solitary rounds."—J. C. MACDONALD

Her face was as kind and gentle as his own mother's

THE STORY OF
Florence Nightingale

By MARGARET LEIGHTON

Illustrated by CORINNE BOYD DILLON

ENID LAMONTE MEADOWCROFT
Supervising Editor

PUBLISHERS Grosset & Dunlap NEW YORK

This book is dedicated to
Jamie, Kim, and Chris,
with love

Contents

CONTENTS

Illustrations

THE STORY OF
Florence Nightingale

"But poor Cherry's tired," Florence protested

CHAPTER ONE

Papa to the Rescue

Let me drive now, Flo. If you don't make old Cherry go faster we'll never get home in time," Parthenope said. She took the reins from her younger sister and slapped them up and down on the pony's broad glossy back.

"But poor Cherry's tired," Florence protested. "You shouldn't make him trot uphill when he's pulling this heavy pony cart. Should she, Miss Christie?"

The governess smiled down into the earnest little face under the rose-trimmed bonnet. "Cherry can't be very tired, Florence," she said. "Look how he pricked up his ears and went faster as soon as we turned in through

[*3*]

your gates. He's glad to be going home to his stable and his oats."

"Flo isn't really worrying about Cherry," Parthenope said. "She's just hoping we won't get home in time. She doesn't want to go into the drawing room to meet Mama's guests. She's such a silly, shy thing. She acts more like a baby than a girl who's almost seven."

Florence hung her head. Parthenope was right. Flo was shy. It frightened her to meet strangers. She sighed as she settled back in the pony cart.

Meanwhile Cherry was trotting briskly up the long, curving avenue. At the end of the avenue stood the house where the Nightingale family lived. It was a big house, surrounded by great trees, wide lawns, and beautiful gardens. "Embley Park," the house was called. And in the year 1827 it was as comfortable and pleasant a home as any in all England.

But at that moment it did not look pleasant to Florence. Her heart sank when she saw a maid in a white cap and apron waiting on the steps. Flo climbed slowly down from the pony cart. Even the happy greeting of Dandy, her

[4]

little black-and-white spaniel, did not lift her spirits.

"Please, Miss Christie," the maid said. "Mrs. Nightingale wants Miss Parthe and Miss Flo to change into their best muslin dresses and come down to the drawing room directly."

Parthe ran eagerly up the steps and into the house. But Flo lingered, patting her dog.

"Hurry along, Florence," Miss Christie commanded. "Didn't you hear your mother's message? I must take the pony to the stables. Go up to the nursery at once and ask Nurse Gale to change your dress."

"There's a burr caught in Dandy's fur, here on his ear, Miss Christie," Florence said quickly. "Don't you think I'd better get it out before it makes a sore?"

"I think you had better obey your mother at once," the governess replied. She spoke so firmly that Florence knew she must obey. She went into the house and up to the nursery.

There she found Nurse Gale and Hannah, the nurserymaid, waiting for her. Parthenope was already washing her hands in one of the two big china bowls on the washing stand.

[5]

Hannah poured hot water from a tall metal can into the second bowl for Florence.

"Now please hurry, Miss Flo," Nurse Gale said. "And don't splash about too long. I declare, it's as much as my life's worth to get you clean and fit to be seen!"

While Flo washed, Parthe's everyday dress was changed for her new white muslin. Parthe stood quietly while Nurse Gale brushed her light-brown hair into smooth, carefully arranged curls.

Then it was Flo's turn. But dressing Flo was

not so easy. "Do hold still, miss!" Nurse Gale scolded. "You're dressed at last, but now your sash needs retying. See how nice Miss Parthe looks! Don't you want to look nice, too, for your mama's guests?"

"No, I don't," Florence said, squirming. "I don't want to go down at all. I have lots better things to do up here. I—I need to change the bandage on my doll. And—"

Parthenope interrupted her. *"Your* doll? It's mine, and you know it."

"You threw it away after you broke it. You said you didn't want it any more," Florence cried.

"But I *do* want it now, and it's still mine," Parthenope declared.

Tears stood in Florence's eyes. "It isn't fair. She only wants it since I mended it!" she exclaimed.

"Stop your quarreling, you naughty girls!" Nurse Gale said. "Your mama is waiting, I tell you." She hustled them out of the room and followed them down the stairs.

At the drawing-room door Florence drew

[7]

back. "What if I do something wrong before all those people?" she thought. "What if I say something that makes them laugh at me?" Her heart began to beat so fast that she could hardly breathe.

But Nurse Gale pushed her from behind and Parthe held tight to her hand. The door opened and she went in.

The laughter and talk in the room stopped suddenly as the two little sisters curtsied in the doorway. Two little girls in white muslin dresses, blue sashes, and lace-trimmed pantalettes. What a pretty picture they made!

Parthe crossed the room at once to where their beautiful, fashionably dressed mother sat among her guests. Flo followed close behind her. But the room, her mother, and even the little frosted cakes on the table looked blurred to poor Flo's frightened eyes. There were so many, many staring strangers!

Somehow she managed to keep near Parthe and to do as her sister did. She curtsied to each guest and repeated each name as her mother introduced her. At last it was over and she was

The two little sisters curtsied in the doorway

safely back at her mother's side once more.

"How charming your children are, my dear Fanny!" a high-voiced lady exclaimed. "Parthenope is so well mannered. And little Flo! Such lovely red-gold hair. Such a complexion. She's a real little beauty!"

"In no time at all they'll be grown-up young ladies," said a gentleman with whiskers and a red face. "Then you'll be taking them up to London to parties and balls. How many hearts do you plan to break at your first ball, little Flo?" he asked. And he pulled one of her smooth-brushed curls.

Florence looked up, her gray eyes round. "Oh, none, sir," she replied. "I'll never break anybody's heart. But if I did, by mistake," she added bravely, "I would bandage it up again."

There was a deafening roar of laughter. "Oh, I *did* say something stupid," Florence thought. "They're laughing at me, just as I was afraid they would." Tears filled her eyes. She hid her face against Nurse Gale's smooth starched apron.

"Why, Flo!" said a deep, beloved voice. Flo

felt herself lifted into her father's strong, comforting arms. She buried her face in his shoulder as he carried her from the room.

"What did I say that was so wrong, Papa?" she asked when the drawing-room door was shut behind them. "Why did they laugh at me?"

Without replying, her father took her into the library and set her down. She loved this room more than any other room in the house. Books filled the shelves from floor to ceiling. Their leather bindings and the wood fire burning on the hearth gave out a pleasant smell.

Mr. Nightingale searched along the shelves and lifted out a heavy volume. He sat down in an armchair and drew Florence onto his lap.

"This is a book on anatomy," he said. "It shows how the human body is made."

He leafed through the pages. "Here is a picture of the heart, Flo," he went on. "See how it lies deep within the chest? It's surrounded by the ribs. You couldn't put a bandage on it, no matter how it was hurt, could you?"

He laid the book on the table. "When people speak of a broken heart, as Colonel Evans did," he continued, "they do not mean an injury to the heart itself, Flo. They mean a hurt to a person's feelings."

In his quiet, careful way Mr. Nightingale explained the puzzle to his little daughter. When he had finished he leaned back in his chair. "Now do you understand? They were not laughing at you, Flo, but at the two different meanings of the words."

In answer Flo flung her arms about his neck and hugged him with all her might. "Oh, I do love you so much, Papa!" she whispered. Suddenly in spite of herself she was crying again.

Mr. Nightingale stroked her hair gently for a while. Then he stood up and set Flo on her feet. "Now the tears are gone," he said. "I think that you and I should go back to your mama's guests. I'm sure they are saving some of those little frosted cakes for you."

The tall man and the small girl returned to the drawing room together. Mr. Nightingale set a low footstool close beside his own chair for Florence.

The cakes were passed to her. She ate two, and they tasted very good. She was hardly frightened at all, now. She knew that she could reach up and slip her hand into her father's whenever she wished.

CHAPTER TWO

Daydreams

WHAT are you doing here all alone, Flo dear?" Mrs. Nightingale asked. She stood in the doorway of Florence's room. "You should be out getting the fresh air on such a beautiful day as this."

Ten-year-old Florence did not answer. She sat at her small writing table with her quill pen in her hand. But she was not writing. Her eyes were fixed on the patch of sky and the green trees outside her window.

"Flo!" Mrs. Nightingale spoke more sharply.

Florence gave a start. Her thoughts had been far away. She stared dumbly at her mother.

[*14*]

Mrs. Nightingale frowned. "Really, Flo, you *must* answer me when I speak to you."

"But—but I didn't hear what you said, Mama," Flo stammered in reply.

Her mother pressed her lips tightly together. "I must be patient with the child," she thought. "But these daydreams of hers are getting worse and worse. What *can* be the matter with her?"

Aloud she said, "I asked what you were doing indoors on this lovely spring day."

Florence's face brightened. "Oh, Mama, I was making a little book. See? It's for my dolls."

Mrs. Nightingale crossed the room. Her full skirts rustled about her as she moved. The tiny book was made of sheets of paper carefully sewn together. It wasn't much larger than a postage stamp.

A prescription for medicine was written in it.

"Nurse Gale told me how to write it," Flo explained. Her gray eyes were shining. "I'm going to ask the doctor for more prescriptions

"But now I want you to go out into the fresh air,"
Mrs. Nightingale said

next time he comes. Then I'll know what to do for my dolls, no matter what ails them."

She hesitated, then continued shyly. "And just now I was thinking that perhaps I could use my prescriptions for real people, too. Aunt Mai's little Blanche had the colic so badly when they were visiting here. Perhaps I might have—"

"That's a very nice thought, my dear," Mrs. Nightingale said. She patted Flo's curls with her smooth, soft hand. "But now I want you to go out into the fresh air. Parthe is waiting for you. She is out under the great beech tree, in the swing."

Florence's eyes clouded. "Parthe can swing just as well by herself," she said rebelliously. "She knows I'm very busy with something *really* important."

Nurse Gale and Hannah came hurrying into the room with their arms full of clean linen. They arrived just in time to hear Flo's reply.

"Miss Flo!" Nurse Gale cried. "Is that the way to answer your dear mama? Shame on you!

[*17*]

Really, madam, sometimes I don't know what to make of her."

"Just make sure that she goes out into the garden at once, Nurse," Mrs. Nightingale said. She swept out of the room. The sweet fragrance of her perfume drifted on the air behind her.

"Why must you always be so contrary, Miss Flo?" said Nurse Gale. "Miss Parthe, she's so nice and easygoing. She never argues or makes trouble for anyone. Why don't you try to be like her?"

"Oh, Parthe!" Flo stamped her foot and her eyes flashed. "Why won't she let me alone? Just because I wouldn't come out and push her in the swing she went complaining to Mama!"

Hurriedly she thrust her little book into a drawer of her writing table. She set the quill pen in place and banged the cover on the inkwell. "Parthe knew how much I wanted to finish my book!" she said.

"Now, now, Miss Flo—" Nurse Gale began.

But Florence did not wait. She flung out of the room, slamming the door behind her.

[*18*]

"There. Wouldn't you know it? She's gone off without her bonnet," Nurse Gale said to Hannah. "She's that careless with her clothes and her looks. She'll have no complexion left if she goes out in the sun without her bonnet."

"I'll take it to her, Mrs. Gale," Hannah said. "There's one good thing about Miss Flo," she added. "She's neat and careful with everything except her clothes. Did you see how nice she put her writing things away, all upset like she was?"

Florence ran down the wide stairs and out of doors. She found Parthe sitting primly in the swing that hung from a limb of the great beech tree. The shadows of the leaves made a pattern of sun and shade on the lawn under her feet.

"Where's your bonnet, Flo?" Parthe asked at once.

Flo tossed her red-gold curls angrily. "I left it in the house," she said. "I can't see or hear with that big floppy thing on my head."

"But you'll get sunburned!" Parthe protested.

[*19*]

"I don't care!"

Parthe looked shocked. "But it'll spoil your complexion. Mama says there's nothing so important in all the world for a girl as her complexion!"

Florence drew in her breath quickly to reply. But she let it out again without speaking. She had started to say, "That's a silly thing to believe!" and she had stopped just in time. "Parthe would have gone straight to Mama telling tales on me if I had said that," she thought.

Now Hannah arrived with the missing bonnet. For once Flo stood quietly while Hannah put it on her and tied the strings under her chin.

The little girl's thoughts were busy and troubled. "Mama, Miss Christie, Parthe, Nurse Gale, and even Hannah all believe that clothes and complexions are *so* important," she said to herself. "I don't think so at all. I really don't."

"Flo!" Parthe was calling to her. "Flo! Wake up. Don't stand there mooning like that.

Come and give the swing a push. I'll push you in it, afterwards."

Florence blushed guiltily. "I've been day-dreaming again, and Mama says it's naughty," she thought. She hurried to push Parthe in the swing. She shoved so hard that the swing flew high and Parthe squealed with delight.

Then it was Flo's turn. The wild, free rush of air cooled her hot cheeks. For a time, at least, she forgot her worries.

Meanwhile, inside the house Mrs. Nightingale had finished giving the orders for the day to her housekeeper. Now she hurried down the stairs to her husband's library.

He looked up from the high desk where he liked to stand to do his writing. "What is it, my dear?" he asked.

"It's about Flo, William," she said. "I'm worried. Her strange way of falling into long daydreams is getting worse and worse. We must try to stop it."

Flo's father laid down his quill pen. "Can we forbid a child to dream?" he asked.

"No, I didn't mean that," Mrs. Nightingale

answered. "I think it might help if we gave her something entirely new to think about. A change of scene, perhaps."

Mr. Nightingale frowned. He loved the quiet of his library, and he hated change of any kind. "It's too early to go to Derbyshire," he said. "Lea Hurst will be cold and windy for several months yet. We always stay here at Embley Park until summer is well begun."

"No, no," Flo's mother said, shaking her head. "Not Lea Hurst. Some place entirely new to Flo. Why not to my brother, Octavius, in London?"

Mr. Nightingale raised his eyebrows. "London? That would be a change of scene indeed!"

"That's exactly what I mean," his wife said eagerly. "A visit to London should fill the thoughts of any country child. Octavius' boy, Freddy, is nearly Flo's age and he gets on well with her. He'll be a lively playmate. The more I think of it the better I like the idea. Flo and Parthe have been quarreling far too much, lately. A separation will do them both good.

[*22*]

Parthe squealed with delight

"I shall take Parthe to Fair Oak to visit her cousin Hilary, and then take Flo on to London."

"As you wish, my dear Fanny," Mr. Nightingale said affectionately. He picked up his pen and went back to his writing.

CHAPTER THREE

Off to London Town!

THE coach is at the door! The coach is at the door!" Florence sang the words over and over. They seemed to keep time with the excited beating of her heart.

She and Parthe were dressed and ready for the journey. They stood waiting in the hall at Embley Park while Nurse Gale fluttered nervously about them. She settled their bonnets straight and smoothed their cloaks. Then she wiped her eyes on the corner of her apron.

"I'll miss you both sadly, my lambs. Now be sure to mind your manners, and don't put me to shame," she warned them.

Miss Christie hurried in. She brought each

of her pupils a going-away present. Two neat little leather writing cases! "Just to make certain you don't forget to write to me." She said, smiling.

Now Mrs. Nightingale came sweeping down the stairway. Her skirts billowed about her as she moved. She wore a linen traveling cloak to keep off the dust. A thick veil covered her bonnet.

Behind her came Clémence, her French maid. Clémence was dressed smartly in black and she carried her mistress' handbag and jewel case.

"Come, girls," Mrs. Nightingale said. "It's time we started."

Outside on the driveway their father was looking over the four coach horses and talking with the driver.

"You'll stop at our regular posting inns for fresh horses," he directed. "The weather has been fine all week. With no mud on the roads to slow you down, you should make good time."

"Yes, sir," the coachman answered. "I

wouldn't be surprised if we made a good ten miles an hour, on the average, sir."

The footmen finished strapping the chests and boxes in their places. A groom opened the door of the roomy coach and let down the folding steps. Mr. Nightingale gave the two lead horses each a pat. He turned to help his wife into the carriage.

Suddenly Flo's little spaniel, Dandy, came bounding gaily out of the house. Before anyone could stop him he had jumped into the coach. He sat looking through the glass window. His red tongue hung far out and he panted happily.

"Dandy thinks he's going with us!" Parthe cried, giggling.

"Take him out at once, Peters," Mrs. Nightingale ordered. "He'll leave hairs on the cushions."

The footman picked Dandy up by the scruff of his neck and dropped him on the ground. The little dog was startled by such treatment. He ran whimpering to Flo with his tail between his legs.

"Oh, poor Dandy!" Flo cried. "He's *so* disappointed. Mayn't we take him along, Mama?"

"Take your dog in the coach to London?" Mrs. Nightingale exclaimed. "Certainly not!"

"Why not? I'll take care of him. I'll hold him on my lap. He won't bother anyone," Florence begged. "Or—" her face brightened, "or I can ride outside with the footmen and hold him. I'd love that."

The color rose in Mrs. Nightingale's cheeks. "Really, Flo, must you be so ridiculous? Give the dog to Peters and climb inside at once."

But now Florence's own cheeks were red. She set her chin stubbornly. "Maybe not all the way to London," she persisted. "Maybe only as far as Fair Oak. Cousin Hilary will be glad to keep him there for me. She loves dogs, too. Then he won't feel so sad and lonely."

"Heaven grant me patience!" Mrs. Nightingale cried. "Was there ever such a naughty, willful child? We will *not* take Dandy in the coach, and that is final."

"Then I shan't go either!" Florence's voice trembled. She planted her feet firmly on the graveled drive as though she were trying to take root there.

"Florence." Her father spoke quietly. "You are not acting like my sensible little daughter. Stop a moment to think. Would Dandy like a journey in a jolting, rocking coach? Most dogs don't. Many of them are made sick by even a short ride. As for leaving him with Cousin Hilary, remember that your uncle keeps mastiffs and fighting bull terriers. They would make short work of a strange little dog brought suddenly among them."

"Oh," Florence answered. All of her anger seemed to melt away. "Well, I suppose you're right, Papa."

"Now give me a kiss and get into the carriage," Mr. Nightingale told her. "And I hope you will try not to distress your mother any more on this journey."

Florence obeyed and the others followed. The step was folded into place and the door was shut with a bang. The two footmen let go the horses' heads and jumped upon their step behind the coach. The driver cracked his whip.

"Good-by, good-by!" Mother and daughters waved their handkerchiefs from the window. Down the long driveway rolled the coach with its four prancing horses.

The travelers stopped for a few days' visit at Fair Oak, Mrs. Nightingale's sister's home. When it was time for Mrs. Nightingale and Flo to leave, Parthe began to pout.

"*I* should be the one to go to London, not you, Flo," she said. "I'm a year older."

"Let's get Mama to change her plans," Flo said eagerly. "I'd much rather stay here with Hilary. I love her the best of all our cousins."

Parthe was silent for a moment. "No," she said. "I've changed my mind. I like Hilary best, too. When you're here, you two are always together. Now *I'll* have a chance to play with her by myself."

[*31*]

So Mrs. Nightingale, Clémence, and Flo traveled on in the coach again. Mrs. Nightingale complained of the dust and Clémence complained of the rocking motion of the coach. But Flo loved every minute of the journey.

She liked it best of all when they stopped to change horses. How quickly the stablemen at the posting inns worked! They shifted the harness from the tired horses to the fresh animals before the dust had time to settle around them.

Then the coachman cracked his whip and away they went again. Behind them the stablemen cheered and waved their hats.

At last they reached the outskirts of great, smoky, noisy London. The horses had to go slowly now. The coach wound through narrow, crooked streets. It threaded its way among crowds of carts, cabs, wagons, and coaches, past great churches and fine houses and buildings.

But all of London was not grand and beautiful. Through the coach windows Flo saw

[32]

many dark tenements and slums. And more ragged, dirty people than she had ever seen before in her life.

It was late when the coach stopped at the home of Octavius Smith, Mrs. Nightingale's brother. The gaslights of London were already glowing through the smoky fog. The travelers were tired and stiff and thickly coated with dust.

They were welcomed by Uncle Octavius and his family. His house was called Thames Bank, he told Flo. The famous river Thames flowed past, almost at his door.

Flo looked eagerly about the room which was to be hers during her visit. "So I'm really in London at last!" she thought.

The square, candlelit room was very like the bedrooms at Embley Park and Lea Hurst. The high, four-poster bed had a ruffled canopy over the top. There was a tall wardrobe and several chairs and chests of drawers. All were made of dark, polished mahogany. The washing stand held a flowered china pitcher and a bowl.

[33]

Clémence unpacked Flo's clothes and put them away for her. While the Frenchwoman worked, Flo looked at herself in the mirror.

She gave a cry of dismay. "Oh, how dirty I am!" she exclaimed. "I can hardly see my face."

"It is always so when traveling, mademoiselle," Clémence said, shrugging her shoulders. "Dust, dust, dust! But they will bring you hot water soon. Do you think you can bathe yourself, Mademoiselle Flo? Madame your mother is waiting for me."

"Yes, I can bathe myself," Flo said proudly. "I can even wash my own back. But Parthe still has to ask Nurse Gale to wash hers for her."

"That's good then, chérie," Clémence said, smiling. "I'll come and do your hair for you while Madame is resting. You are to eat supper with your cousin Freddy, in his schoolroom."

Two housemaids brought Flo's hot water almost as soon as Clémence had gone. They spread a bath sheet on the floor and brought the round tin bathtub out of the closet for her.

It was all exactly as the servants did every day at home. London was not so different from Embley Park, after all.

Flo bathed and dressed herself. She was beginning to brush her hair when Clémence returned.

"No, no, mademoiselle. You must let *me* arrange your hair," Clémence said. "Madame wants you to look your best for her brother and his family."

When Flo was ready, Clémence showed her the way to the schoolroom. Although Flo knew Freddy well, she paused a moment at the schoolroom door. She felt suddenly shy.

"Will Freddy be different?" she wondered. "And whatever can I think of to talk about with him?"

Freddy was tossing a little ball from one hand to the other when Florence entered. He had grown since his last visit to Embley. He was younger than Flo, but he was now as tall as she and much broader.

"Hello, Flo," he said. "Do you like boating? Because we're going on the river tomorrow.

[35]

"Hello, Flo," Freddy said. "Do you like boating?"

Papa will row us. I can row, too. There are three real steamboats that pass here every day. Their names are the *Diana,* the *Fly,* and the *Endeavor."*

Before Flo had a chance to reply, Freddy continued. "I like the *Fly* best because it has the tallest smokestack and makes the most smoke. Do you like jam tart? We're having it for dessert. Supper's only mutton, but we'll get some of the grownups' dessert, too, when we go down to say good night to them."

Freddy was like all of Mama's people, Flo thought. Cheerful and talkative. "I needn't have worried about what to say to him," she told herself. "And I needn't worry about going into the dining room to meet the grownups, either. Freddy will talk all the time and no one will notice me at all!"

CHAPTER FOUR

A Visit and a Surprise

MRS. NIGHTINGALE and Clémence remained only a few days in London. Then they
returned in the coach to Fair Oak. Flo stayed
on at her uncle Octavius Smith's house beside
the busy river Thames.

Every day when the weather was fine Mr.
Smith took Flo and Freddy boating on the
river. Big, kindly Uncle Oc was a fine oarsman.
Freddy liked to row, too. He worked hard to
keep pace with his father.

Flo sat happily in the stern seat of the boat.
She wore her bonnet, but she let it fall back on
her shoulders. "The sun here in smoky London can't be strong enough to sunburn anyone," she decided.

She loved the feeling of the wind blowing in her face as they skimmed over the bright water. She loved to watch the different kinds of vessels that passed them, going to and fro. The river was like a broad, busy highway.

"What is that great building that stands all by itself, Fred?" Flo asked.

"That's Milbank Prison," Freddy told her. "There are hundreds of wicked criminals locked up in there." Freddy liked to show off his knowledge of London to his country cousin.

Flo's eyes widened. "Do—do any of them ever get out?" she asked. The prison looked dangerously near to her uncle's house.

"Oh no, they keep them locked up tight," Freddy assured her.

Uncle Oc paused in his rowing and rested on his oars. "That particular prison is new. It is well built, and they say it is so comfortable that the prisoners don't want to escape," he told them. "That may not be true. But it is true that it is much better than any other jail in England.

[*39*]

"That's Milbank Prison," Freddy told her

"Whenever I see it, it reminds me of what one good citizen can do for his fellow creatures," he added.

"What do you mean, Uncle Oc?" Flo asked.

Uncle Oc took off his hat and wiped his forehead with his handkerchief. "I'm thinking of a man named John Howard," he answered.

"John Howard? Who's he, Papa?" Freddy asked.

"He was an Englishman who lived here in London," his father replied. "Before his day, prisons and jails were horrible dungeons. John Howard started working to make them places where criminals could learn a better way of living."

"Does he live here in London now?" Florence asked.

"No," her uncle replied. "He died years ago. But lately his work has been taken up again and carried on by a lady."

"A lady?" Flo echoed in great surprise.

"Yes, a good, brave, religious lady. Her name is Mrs. Elizabeth Fry. She has devoted herself to working among prisoners," Uncle Oc told her.

"A lady!" Flo repeated again in amazement. She had never dreamed that a lady could do such things. Ladies were supposed to stay at home and be waited upon by servants. Not to go out and work among wicked prisoners!

Freddy interrupted her thoughts suddenly. "Look!" he shouted. "Here comes a steamer. It's the *Diana!*"

Uncle Oc quickly brought the boat about. He headed it to meet the waves made by the larger vessel's passing. "Yes, it's the *Diana,*" he agreed.

Flo clung to her seat as they bobbed up and down in the steamer's wake. She waved to the passengers and laughed as gaily as Freddy.

But in her mind the name, Elizabeth Fry, rang like a thrilling chord of music. It was a name which she would not forget.

When Flo returned to her family, more than a month later, they had already moved to Lea Hurst. This was their summer home in northern England. It stood high on a windy hill. The gardens around it were built on terraces, one lower than the other. Far below them all ran the rushing waters of the river Derwent.

The bare, breezy hills of Derbyshire had never appeared so beautiful to Flo as they did after her stay in hot, smoky London. Her mother had never looked lovelier. Her father seemed taller and kinder than ever.

As for Parthe, Flo felt such a surprising flood of love at the sight of her that she almost covered her with kisses.

There was dear Miss Christie, too, and Nurse Gale. And Dandy! The little dog trembled with joy when she hugged him. When she let him go he raced round and round her like a wild creature.

"Dandy missed you so much," Parthe told her. "Whenever one of us spoke your name he ran to look for you. Flo, there's a wonderful surprise. I could hardly keep it secret when I wrote to you. Come, you must see!"

Parthe took her hand and they ran together down to the stables, while their father fol-

[43]

They ran together down to the stables

lowed more slowly. Cherry, the fat old pony, whinnied as they came into the sweet, hay-scented dimness. Florence stopped to rub his soft nose.

"Where is the surprise?" she asked. "Is it kittens? Are they Tabitha's?"

"Kittens? Oh, no! Look in the next stalls," Parthe cried. She was dancing up and down with excitement.

Beyond Cherry's stall were the large open box stalls. In them stood two beautiful little saddle horses. Flo stared with her mouth open. She was too amazed to speak.

"The chestnut is named Robin and he's mine," Parthe explained. "The bay mare is yours. Her name is Swallow. Papa bought them especially for us. They aren't ponies, they're horses. He's going to teach us to ride. And Mama has had new riding habits made for us, too."

Flo could only stand and stare. Then the bay mare put her head over the edge of her stall door and whinnied softly.

Flo moved nearer and held out her hand.

[45]

Swallow's breath blew in and out. It felt warm on Flo's fingers.

"Our riding habits have long, full skirts, just like Mama's," Parthe told her happily. "Mine is crimson and yours is green. Mama got boots for us, too, and little hats with feathers to match the habits."

Flo was stroking Swallow's glossy neck. "You're a *beauty!*" she whispered into the delicate, pointed ear. "I can't believe that you belong to me. Your nose is softer than velvet. I think you like me already."

"Of course she does," Mr. Nightingale said, smiling as he entered the stable. "And tomorrow morning we'll all go for a ride before breakfast. So mind that you wake up early!"

CHAPTER FIVE

The New Cousin

IN FLO'S room Nurse Gale and Parthe together were helping Flo into her new riding habit. When the last hook was fastened, Flo looked at herself in the mirror. She could hardly believe that the tall young lady she saw was really herself!

The fine broadcloth habit fitted her smoothly. She looked with wonder from the tips of her small, polished boots to the smart little hat on her head. The green feather curled prettily against her shining red-gold hair.

Parthe was looking at Flo, too. But she had begun to frown. "Oh dear," she complained.

"I wish *I'd* chosen the green instead of the crimson."

"I'll change with you. I like red just as well," Flo began.

But Nurse Gale shook her head. "No, Miss Flo," she said. "Your mama chose the colors. Miss Parthe couldn't wear the green so well. She's too pale. But with your bright complexion, dearie, you can wear anything."

Parthe looked crosser than ever. Then her face cleared. "Well, anyway, I can ride better than you, Flo," she stated. "I've already been out with Papa lots of times. He's taught me how to trot and even to canter."

But after a few weeks of practice Flo was able to ride as well as Parthe. Swallow was gentle and easy to control. Soon father and daughters were cantering their horses every day over the rolling, windy hills.

The three came home from an early ride one morning. As they approached the house Flo exclaimed, "Look! There's a carriage going up our avenue. I wonder whose it is."

"That looks like your uncle Sam Smith's

Parthe looked crosser than ever

new light chaise," Mr. Nightingale said. He spurred his horse to a gallop and the girls followed at the same pace.

"Why is Uncle Sam arriving at this time in the morning?" Flo wondered. "I hope nothing's wrong with Aunt Mai or little Blanche!" Aunt Mai was Flo's favorite of all her aunts.

The driver of the chaise was not Flo's uncle, however. He was a groom who had been sent with a letter. The letter brought good news. Aunt Mai had just had a new baby boy.

But best of all, Aunt Mai wished Flo to come for a visit. She had sent the carriage especially to fetch her back.

"Flo has such a way with babies," Aunt Mai's letter said. "Our little Blanche has been sadly spoiled, I'm afraid, and now she's more than we can manage. Flo can help me by keeping her happy for me. She can even help care for our new baby. We are naming him William Shore Smith."

"May I go? Oh, *do* say I may go, Mama!" Florence begged. "But what's the matter? Aren't you pleased?"

"Of course I'm pleased. And I think it will be very nice for you to go," Mrs. Nightingale answered. "But it would have been nicer if Parthe had been invited, too."

"But Parthe isn't so fond of babies as Flo is," their father said. "She wasn't always kind to little Blanche when they were here."

"I don't care!" Parthe tossed her head. "I'd rather not go, anyway. I don't see what Flo finds so fascinating about babies. All wet flannel and sour milk!"

"It's because they are so helpless and tiny and need care so much," Flo tried to explain.

"Well, I just don't like horrid smells, and that's that," Parthe declared.

"Neither do I. That's why I want to clean them up and put them to rights," Flo answered. "Not run away and pretend everything is lovely!"

"Girls, girls! There's no time for arguments now," Mrs. Nightingale interrupted. "The chaise is waiting to take you back, Flo. You must hurry and get ready for your journey."

The ride in the swift carriage was fully as

exciting as the journey to London had been. By nightfall Flo was at her uncle's home.

She loved the new baby the minute she saw him. And she did so well at keeping Blanche happy that the little girl followed her wherever she went.

One day Flo sat in a chair in Aunt Mai's nursery. In her arms she was holding a warm, living bundle, her tiny cousin, Shore Smith.

"He's adorable!" Flo said, leaning over him fondly. "And he's *my* boy, aren't you?" One of her curls brushed across his pink button of a nose. His face screwed up. The tiniest sneeze in the world burst out of him.

"Did you hear that?" Flo cried. Her eyes were shining. "Only three weeks old, and already he knows how to sneeze perfectly!"

Nurse Emmons, who was bustling about the nursery, chuckled. And Aunt Mai smiled from her armchair, among her lacy pillows.

"I told you, Emmons, that Miss Flo was wonderful with babies," she said.

The nurse nodded. "Some has the gift for it and some hasn't, madam," she said.

[52]

"Where did you learn how to be a nurse, Emmons?" Flo asked. "Did you learn in a hospital?"

Nurse Emmons frowned and drew herself up stiffly. "A hospital? I should say not!" she answered. "I'm a respectable woman. I would never so much as set my foot inside one of them places. If you were older you'd never ask me such a question. A hospital, indeed!"

"I'm sure Miss Flo meant no harm, Emmons," Aunt Mai said hastily. "But Flo dear, hospitals are dreadful places. Nobody ever goes into one who can possibly be cared for at home. Hospital nurses are not the good, careful women we must have to take charge of our precious children."

"I'm sorry, Emmons," Flo stammered. "I only wondered how a person could ever learn. I mean, learn all the things one must know to take good care of a little baby."

Mrs. Emmons smiled good-naturedly again. "That's all right, Miss Flo, no offense," she said. "If you want to learn, just watch me and welcome. That's the way I learned. I was nurserymaid to an experienced baby nurse. That's the way most of us teach ourselves."

"Oh, Emmons!" Flo cried. "I've watched you bathe Shore so often. Do you suppose I could give him his bath today?"

Nurse Emmons looked into the eager face. "Well, I don't know," she began. "What do you think, madam?"

"I think Flo could do it very well," Aunt Mai answered, smiling.

"Well then, Miss Flo, let's see how you begin," the nurse said. "I'll hold the little man while you get ready."

Flo's eyes were sparkling and her cheeks were red. "First I'll make sure that there's a good fire on the hearth and that the room is warm," she said.

The two women watched her stir up the fire. She hung the baby's clean clothes and soft flannels on a rack to air and warm them. She moved a low, armless chair closer to the fire. Beside it she set the baby's bath basin and pitchers of hot and cold water.

Carefully she mixed the hot and cold water,

[54]

testing it with her elbow to make sure of the temperature. She seated herself, then jumped up again. "Your lap is bigger than mine. I'd better have a pillow to hold him on," she said. "Now I'm ready!"

Nurse Emmons was beaming as she laid the baby on Flo's pillowed lap. "Now there's what I call a clever girl," she said. "She thought up the pillow herself, madam. All the rest she learned from me, but that was her own idea, and a good one, too."

Flo's hands trembled a little as she dipped a soft piece of old flannel into the warm water. Carefully she washed the baby's face, then his neck and ears. His skin was rosy-red and un-believably soft. "How prettily his fingers curl into tiny fists," she thought, as she tried to uncurl and wash them.

At last it was over. Baby Shore was warm and clean and smiling. Flo herself was damp with perspiration. But she had never been so proud and happy in all her life.

The days passed swiftly. Flo was sorry when her father arrived to take her home. They

Nurse Emmons laid the baby on Flo's pillowed lap

reached Lea Hurst only a little while before the family moved back to Embley Park for the winter months. There Flo and Parthe learned that Miss Christie was ill. She could no longer teach them their lessons.

"I shall teach the girls myself," said Mr. Nightingale. "They both have good brains. And we will enjoy working together."

CHAPTER SIX

A Darker Side of the World

MR. NIGHTINGALE was a careful, patient teacher. But he expected hard work from his daughters.

"We shall study history, philosophy, mathematics, Latin, Greek, French, and German," he told them. "And Italian, too, of course. Your mother and I were living in Italy when you both were born. I want you to learn to love the beautiful Italian language as much as I do."

Father and daughters were sitting at the library table one autumn afternoon many months later. Flo's head was bent over her book. She really enjoyed working out difficult problems. Arithmetic and even Greek grammar fascinated her just as interesting puzzles did.

But Parthe was tired and bored. Her eyes kept straying to the window. She could see bright autumn leaves blowing in the wind beyond the panes of glass. She moved restlessly in her chair.

The door opened and their mother rustled in. She wore her bonnet and shawl. Her husband rose politely from his chair and Parthe jumped up also. She was glad of any interruption. But Flo was too deeply absorbed in her work to notice that anyone had come in.

"The girls have been indoors long enough, William," Mrs. Nightingale said. "I am going down to our village to take a basket of food to one of your tenants, Mrs. Hodge. The poor woman's ill again, the Vicar told me. Do let the girls come along. This is the first fine day we've had this week."

Parthe hurried out of the room and up the stairs. But Flo shook her head. "If you don't mind, Mama, I'd rather finish this translation

[59]

now," she said. "I'm just beginning to figure out what was bothering me before."

"Flo has been making good progress in her Greek," her father said. "Very soon now we shall begin to read Homer."

Mrs. Nightingale smiled. "Whatever is the use of our girls troubling their minds with so much study?" she asked. "When they begin to go to parties and balls they'll forget it all soon enough."

"I think it is important to keep their minds busy," Flo's father said. "Flo's only thirteen. She's not ready yet for parties or balls."

"There's plenty to fill the mind of a girl of her age in learning to help about the house," Mrs. Nightingale said. "For one thing, knowing how to arrange the flowers every day in the vases is important. Parthe already does it beautifully. She's of great assistance to me, too, in entertaining my guests. If Flo didn't always have her nose in a Greek or Latin grammar, she might be as helpful as her sister."

"But—" Flo began to protest.

"Now, no arguments please, Flo," her

mother said firmly. "Do as I ask and go put on your bonnet and shawl. We musn't keep the horses standing."

When Flo came outdoors, ready to go, Parthe and her mother were already in the carriage. The footman helped Flo in. Then he jumped to his place beside the coachman. The glossy, spirited horses went prancing down the drive. Their harness jingled with every step.

They stopped in front of Mrs. Hodge's small thatch-roofed cottage, and several children came running out. They stared at the carriage and the fine horses.

Mrs. Nightingale got out. She gathered up her skirts from the dust of the path. "You needn't come in, girls, unless you wish to," she told her daughters.

"I shan't go in," Parthe said, wrinkling her nose. "Those cottages are always so stuffy. I brought my sketching pad and pencils. I'll stay here and draw the ivy climbing over that cottage chimney."

But Flo followed her mother up the path. One of the dirty, tousle-headed children had

Flo followed her mother up the path

darted back into the cottage. Now the door was opened by a girl of about Flo's own age. She held a heavy baby in her thin arms.

She curtsied to Mrs. Nightingale. "Please come inside, ma'am," she said. "Ma's in the bed. She asks you to excuse her not getting up, but she's so weak. The doctor says she's to stay quiet."

"Of course, that's quite all right, Sarah," Mrs. Nightingale answered.

Flo and her mother went into the cottage. The footman followed, carrying a basket. Behind him trooped all the silent, ragged children.

The inside of the cottage was dim and smoky. Flo could see nothing at first except a low fire burning under an iron pot on the hearth. The air was stifling.

Soon Flo's eyes became used to the darkness. Then she saw that all the children were now huddled round a bed in a corner of the single room.

On the bed lay a woman with flushed, sunken cheeks. "It's very good of you to come, ma'am," the woman said in a hoarse whisper.

"Well, Mrs. Hodge, I was sorry to hear that you are ill again," Mrs. Nightingale said. "I've brought you some nourishing broth and some jelly."

"Thank you, ma'am," the woman said. Tears stood in her eyes. "Thank you for being a kind, charitable lady."

"I'm glad to see that your Sarah is here," Mrs. Nightingale went on. "She takes good care of you and the younger children, doesn't she? The Vicar thought perhaps you should be sent to the hospital. But—"

"The hospital?" Mrs. Hodge's hoarse voice was suddenly shrill with fear. "Oh no, ma'am. No, not the hospital. I've heard how they treat poor, unlucky people there. Don't let them send me off to die among strangers!"

"No, we shan't do that. That's exactly what I told the Vicar," Mrs. Nightingale assured her. "I told him you would be getting good care from Sarah."

"Yes, she's a good girl. She'll be leaving, though. Vicar's wife has found her a fine job as

*"I've brought you some nourishing broth
and some jelly"*

a housemaid. It'll be a blessing to have wages come in again, with Hodge gone and me so ailing."

"But who will look after things here, then?" Mrs. Nightingale asked with concern.

"My Nancy, the next one, is almost ten," Mrs. Hodge explained. She lifted her head and peered around the room. "Where's Nancy?" she asked.

"She's gone to the well for water, Ma," one of the children said. "Oh, here she comes now."

Another small, towheaded girl had entered the cottage. She carried a heavy bucket of water.

"Make your curtsey to the gentry, Nan," her mother ordered.

Nan stepped forward and bobbed awkwardly up and down, hanging her head shyly.

"I'm very glad you can help your mother, Nancy," Mrs. Nightingale said. "Now we must go. Come, Flo."

The air outside the cottage smelled deliciously fresh and cool. Flo drew a deep breath of it as she followed her mother and climbed into the carriage.

"Well, wasn't it smelly in there?" Parthe asked with a pert giggle.

"I'm afraid it was," their mother sighed. "It *does* seem to me that the poor could at least be clean."

Troubling thoughts and questions had come crowding into Flo's mind. "But Mama," she said, "it's surely very hard for them to keep clean when they have to carry all their water from the village well, isn't it?

"And that cottage is far too small for such a large family. Couldn't Papa give them a better one? There was no window at all. Shouldn't every cottage have a window?"

Her mother spoke sharply. "Your father is as kind and generous a landlord as there is in the neighborhood. I'm sure he does more for his tenants than anyone around here," she said.

When Flo did not reply, Mrs. Nightingale added, more gently, "It is very sad to think that there must be poor, unfortunate, unhappy people in the world. I know that it distresses you, my dear. But remember what the Bible says. 'The poor always ye have with you.' Only try to be thankful that Heaven has blessed *you* with a comfortable home."

Florence was silent. Her gray eyes looked out over the bronze and gold of the autumn fields. But she did not really see them.

She saw, instead, the poor sick woman in her dark, airless cottage. How could she ever get well in such a place? How could those little girls give her the care she needed?

Flo knew what careful tending the people in her own family received when they were sick. Her mother's gift of broth and jelly would not be of much real help to poor Mrs. Hodge.

"There must be some other, better way to help poor people who are sick," Flo thought. "And some day I'm going to find it."

CHAPTER SEVEN

The Shepherd's Collie

"SHALL we ride in the Forest today, Miss Flo?" the Reverend Mr. Giffard asked.

Mr. Nightingale had gone up to London. While he was away the Vicar of East Wellow was riding daily with Parthe and Flo. Today Parthe was kept indoors with a cold. So Florence and the elderly clergyman started off together. She rode on Swallow, he on his big dapple-gray horse.

"Let's go over the Downs, instead of in the Forest," Flo suggested. "I haven't been there in weeks. I love that high, open country. It reminds me of Lea Hurst."

They followed the avenue to the main highway. Just beyond the gates of Embley

Park they passed a small stone cottage. It was surrounded by walls, sheds, and sheepfolds.

"Smithers has his sheep out grazing early," Florence said. "Perhaps we'll see them up on the Downs. I like to watch his dog, Cap, at work."

"Yes, Cap's a fine collie," the Vicar agreed. "I really don't know what Smithers would do without a good sheep dog. He's getting very feeble."

They went on for a short while in silence. "How gracefully Miss Florence rides," the Vicar thought. "She's growing into a beautiful girl. A serious and intelligent girl, too."

Then he sighed to himself. "Let me see— she's nearly sixteen. What a pity that she must soon become a fashionable young society miss!"

They had reached the crest of a hill. The wide sweep of the Downs lay before them. Across it ran a dusty line of roadway.

"There are the sheep, near the road," Flo said. She pointed with her riding crop. "But whatever is the matter with them?"

The flock was milling about and bleating in confusion.

"There's the shepherd!" the Vicar cried. "There, in the ditch. Is he hurt?"

Florence spurred her horse to where the old man was crouching. "What is it, Smithers? What's the matter?" she cried.

"It's my dog, Cap, Miss Florence," the shepherd answered. His face was twisted with grief. "My poor collie, Cap. He *will* chase after the carts that goes so fast along this road. It was his one fault, and now it's been his death!"

"Death!" Florence echoed. She slid out of her saddle to the ground and bent anxiously over the pitiful, dusty bundle of fur. "Why, no, Smithers," she exclaimed. "He's not dead. He's breathing."

"Yes, Miss Flo. He's still alive but his leg's smashed bad. Poor laddie, he's done for," Smithers said.

He wiped his sleeve across his eyes. "If I had me a stout cord here I could put him out of his misery quick and easy. He'd not feel any pain. Though I'd as soon cut off my own right hand."

"Cap won't bite me, will you, old fellow?" Flo said

"Oh, no!" Flo cried in horror. "A broken leg can be set and mended. Wait." Her soft lips were suddenly firm. She felt the dog's leg tenderly. "I'll set it myself."

The Vicar had dismounted. He, too, was bending anxiously over the collie. Now he caught at Flo's arm. "Be careful, Miss Florence," he warned her. "If you touch him where he's hurt he may bite you. Surely Smithers knows what's best to do, my dear."

"Cap won't bite me, will you, old fellow?" Flo said. The dog's beautiful, intelligent eyes were glazed with pain. But he recognized Flo for a friend. He whined softly and licked at her hand.

"He knows I'm going to help him," Florence said. "See, there's a bad cut on his shoulder, too. But it's not bleeding dangerously. The bone in his leg must be set before we try to move him anywhere."

"Now Miss Flo—" the Vicar began. "Surely you can't—"

"I'm sure I *can*," Forence answered. "I watched the vet set a foxhound's leg just last week."

She turned to the shepherd. "First we must have splints. Smithers, you cut two straight smooth sticks about this long." She measured the length between her forefingers.

When they were brought, Flo nodded approvingly. "Now I must have bandages. Let me use your neckerchief, Smithers. Here's my own scarf. And Vicar, may I have your handkerchief, too?"

"Now *really*, Miss Florence—" the clergyman began once more. But it was plain to him that the girl knew exactly what she was doing. It was plain, too, that she heard nothing and saw nothing but the work under her hands. He passed her the square of white linen.

While the two gray-haired men watched, Flo set the bone skillfully and gently. Then she bound it firmly in place with the splints.

"There!" she said. She sat back on her heels and pushed a strand of her bright hair off her forehead. "See? He feels more comfortable already."

She stood up and brushed the dust from her riding habit. "Now, Smithers, when I'm mounted I want you to lift Cap and put him in front of me on my horse. I'll walk Swallow slowly and get Cap home without jarring him."

When they reached the shepherd's cottage, Flo washed and bandaged the wound on Cap's shoulder. She made a bed for him of soft straw beside the hearth.

"Give him plenty of clean water to drink, and let him rest here where it's warm," she told Mrs. Smithers. "He probably won't want to eat anything for a while."

[75]

The next morning Flo was up and out before the rest of her family was awake. She hurried down the avenue to the stone cottage to visit her patient.

Cap greeted her with bright eyes and a wagging tail. Before many days it was plain to everyone that the shepherd's collie would soon be as sound as ever.

Old Smithers was overjoyed. "I don't know how I could have kept on tending sheep without my Cap," he said. "It's a wonderful thing you've done, Miss Flo. A wonderful thing."

Flo stroked Cap's head. There was a strangely warm and happy feeling in her heart. "I have helped someone out of great trouble," she thought. "And I did it with my own hands!"

CHAPTER EIGHT

The Voice

AUTUMN passed and winter came. The Christmas holidays brought much visiting back and forth among the Nightingales and their relatives. The Nicholson cousins gave the gayest parties of all.

The Nicholsons loved music, dancing, charades, and games. Flo admired her beautiful older cousin, Marianne Nicholson. And Marianne's high spirits drew Flo out of her shyness. She found herself joining into the games and dances as she never had before.

Mr. Nightingale stood looking across the Nicholsons' ballroom one evening. In the candlelight the full-skirted silk frocks of the girls made the room as bright as a flower garden.

"Can that truly be our Flo?" he asked himself in surprise. "She's not a long-legged child any more. She's a tall, graceful young lady!"

He saw that the young men at the party were admiring Flo, also. She always had plenty of partners eager to dance with her.

"You must be very proud of your charming daughter," an older gentleman said to Mr. Nightingale. "Miss Flo is quite the belle of the evening."

The holiday parties ended at last. Back home at Embley Park, lessons began again for Parthe and Flo. In the afternoon they went visiting in the neighborhood with their mother when the weather was fine. When it stormed there was music and reading and embroidery to fill their hours.

The Nightingales entertained many house guests that winter. But one February evening the family was dining alone. Mrs. Nightingale sat at the end of the table, erect and handsome. She and Parthe kept up a lively conversation.

As usual, Mr. Nightingale listened quietly. He smiled and put in a word now and then, but he spoke little.

Flo was silent. Her mind was full of a new experience she had had that afternoon. The Vicar's wife had taken Flo with her on a visit to a poor family in the parish.

"Their little boy, Jackie, is a great pet of mine," the Vicar's wife had said. "He's very ill. He's had a bad attack of the fever. I'm afraid that he gets very little care, however. His mother has no time, with all the other children to look after, too."

When they reached the cottage the good lady had rolled up her sleeves and set to work. Flo helped her. Together they bathed the little boy and changed his bed linen. It was wonderful to see him fall at once to sleep when he was made comfortable.

Now Flo looked about her own dining room, at the gleaming white damask table-cloth, the fine china and shining silver. She thought of the poor, crowded cottage. "How can it be right for me to have so much while they have so little?" she asked herself unhappily.

When dinner was over the Nightingales went to the drawing room. The family settled

[*79*]

into their usual chairs. The fire crackled on the hearth and the gilt clock on the mantel ticked softly.

Mrs. Nightingale spread her embroidery on her lap. She held her strands of wool up to the light and selected the color she wished. Then she threaded her needle and set to work.

Parthe bent over her drawing board. She was finishing a sketch she had made that afternoon.

Mr. Nightingale opened a book of Italian poetry and began to read aloud. His voice went on and on, speaking the musical words. The hands of the clock turned slowly. The fire burned lower.

Flo's own needlework lay idle on her lap. She tried her best to keep her mind on what her father was reading. In spite of herself her thoughts wandered.

"Mrs. Giffard *should* have called in the doctor for Jackie," she thought. "His cough seemed very sharp and painful—"

Flo's thoughts were suddenly interrupted. She realized that her father had paused in his reading, and was speaking to her.

"That's a fine bit of verse there, Flo," he said. "Did you like it? When I first read it to myself I thought that it would please you."

Flo nodded and murmured something polite. Her father opened the book again and continued his reading.

Now Flo was worrying again about little Jackie. "How hot his rough little hands were!" she thought. "Will Mrs. Watts remember to put hot poultices on his chest tonight, as Mrs. Giffard suggested?"

Mr. Nightingale came to the end of his reading and laid the book upon the table. "Let's have some music now, Flo," he said.

"Yes, that last quadrille you learned was pretty and gay," her mother agreed.

Flo went to the piano obediently. Her slim fingers flew over the keys. She played accurately, but tonight there was no spirit in her music. The clock on the mantel struck ten as she finished.

"Thank you, my dear," Mr. Nightingale said. "How pleasant these quiet evenings are! I look forward to many years of them."

A footman now appeared bringing the bed-

Her slim fingers flew over the keys

room candles. Mr. Nightingale kissed Parthe and Flo. "Good night to you, my dears, and pleasant dreams," he said.

Flo kissed her mother and followed Parthe up the broad stairway. In her room a small fire was burning on the hearth. A chambermaid was running a warming pan between her sheets. "Good night, Miss Flo," the maid said, curtseying.

"Good night, Polly," Flo answered.

She undressed and put on her long white nightgown with ruffles at the throat and wrists. She blew out her candle. But she did not get into bed.

Instead she crossed the room and sat beside the window. She pressed her forehead to the cold glass of the windowpane.

"Will it be like this forever?" she thought. "Long, long evenings like this one, over and over again! Or going to one party after another as Mama does, when there are so many poor, miserable people in the world who need help.

"But," she wondered, "what can *I* do to help them? I *must* find a way."

[*83*]

Through the window she could see the moon. It floated high in the sky above a bank of silver-edged clouds. She opened the window, and shivered a little as the chill wind touched her. But still she stayed, watching the bright,

cold disk of the moon. Behind her the fire died down on the hearth.

"I *must* find a way," she repeated to herself desperately.

A moment later Florence was on her feet,

breathless and trembling. She had heard a Voice. But had she *really* heard it? The room was silent now, except for the pounding of her own heart.

For a long time she stood motionless. She was unwilling to move, afraid to break the spell, hoping to hear the Voice again.

At last Flo stirred. She crossed slowly to her desk. By the light of the moon she dipped her pen into the ink and wrote a sentence on a sheet of paper.

"On February 7, 1837, God spoke to me and called me to His service," wrote Florence Nightingale.

CHAPTER NINE

Curtsey to the Queen

THERE, Miss Parthe, how's that?" old Nurse Gale said. She stepped back to give Parthe a better view of her dress in the long glass.

Parthe peered into the hand mirror at the reflection behind her. Her face was unhappy. "No, it's worse than ever!" she cried, flinging the mirror down on the floor.

"Oh, Miss Parthe!" Nurse Gale exclaimed. She picked up the mirror anxiously. "It's not broken, thank goodness! It would mean seven years bad luck if you was to break a mirror, dearie. And on *this* day, of all days!"

It was a great day indeed for the Nightingale girls. They had returned to England after two

[*86*]

years in Europe. They had been finishing their education with foreign travel.

Now, on this warm May afternoon, they were dressing in their London apartment. Soon they would drive to the royal palace. They would be presented to England's newly crowned young Queen, Victoria.

Flo was already dressed. She stood in the middle of the room in her wide-spreading, hoop-skirted gown. She did not dare to sit, for fear of crushing the delicate folds of snow-white silk and lace. On her head was a coronet of curling white plumes.

"But what's wrong, Miss Parthe?" Mrs. Gale asked. "It looks very nice indeed, to me."

"How can an old children's nurse know anything about style?" Parthe snapped. "Where's Mama? Why doesn't she let Clémence help us? *We're* the ones who are to be presented, aren't we?" Her voice was high and shrill.

"Whatever is the matter, girls?" Mrs. Nightingale asked. She came rustling into the room in a gown of violet satin. She wore a jeweled necklace and bracelets, and a jeweled tiara rested on her elaborately dressed hair. Clémence followed her mistress.

"Look at the back of my bodice!" Parthe cried. "It wrinkles and sags. Tell Clémence to make it fit smoothly, like Flo's."

"See what you can do, Clémence," Mrs. Nightingale ordered. "We should be leaving any moment, now."

Clémence shrugged her shoulders. "The dress fits perfectly, madame. The fault is in her own posture. Mademoiselle Flo carries herself beautifully but Mademoiselle Parthe stoops forward. That makes all the difference."

Parthe stamped her foot. Her eyes filled with tears. "It isn't fair!" she sobbed. "Everywhere we went in Europe Flo was the beautiful Miss Nightingale, the popular Miss Nightingale. I was just her older sister. Must it be the same here in England? Must I *always* play second fiddle to her?"

For a moment no one could think of anything to say. Nurse Gale sniffed. Clémence pressed her lips together stubbornly. Mrs. Nightingale looked distressed and uncertain.

[*88*]

"Oh. Parthe!" Flo cried. Her own eyes were wet. "That isn't true. Everyone loves and admires you. You are so clever."

Flo smoothed the silk of her sister's bodice. "Look again," she said soothingly. "Your dress is lovely. It only wrinkles when you screw yourself around to see the back. Oh, Parthe, remember what fun we had in Paris having our dresses made for this day? Now the time has come to wear them. Don't be unhappy!"

Parthe managed a weak smile, and at once the sisters were in each other's arms. "I'm sorry," Parthe said. "But I'm so excited and nervous!"

"So am I," Flo confessed. "I wonder if I'll be able to curtsey to the Queen the way we're supposed to. Let's practice just once more."

Side by side they sank low in the deep court curtsey. Their skirts billowed out around them like the petals of great white flowers.

They rose again, laughing and breathless.

"There, that's better," Mrs. Nightingale said. "Now come. The carriage has been ready this half hour."

[*89*]

They entered their carriage and drove through the London streets. When they drew near the royal palace the horses had to go slowly. Long lines of coaches and carriages blocked the way, all bound for the Queen's reception.

At last they reached the palace entrance. The two girls followed their mother up the carpeted stairs. Flo's heart was beating fast. Her cheeks were pink and her eyes shone. Many heads turned to look at her with admiration as she passed.

In the Queen's anteroom they had to await their turn to be presented. Flo's knees began to tremble under her. She reached for Parthe's hand, and it felt cold as ice. At last a servant called out their names. They followed their mother through the door into the great, crowded throne room.

The high-ceilinged room was filled with beautifully dressed ladies, gentlemen in court costume, and uniformed officers.

At the end of the room the Queen stood near her gilded throne, her courtiers about her.

[*90*]

When Flo's turn came to be presented, she curtsied deeply and gracefully. As she rose she looked with great interest at the Queen. This tiny, slim girl who now ruled England was only a year older than herself.

For a moment Flo's clear gray eyes met Victoria's blue ones. There was friendliness in the little Queen's smile and nod. Two young girls had met for the first time. They would meet again as great and noble women. Both of them were to bring many changes to their world.

After the presentation at court, there was a gay ball. And during the weeks which followed it, there were parties, concerts, theatres and dances in London. Flo was very popular. And wherever she was invited, Parthe of course went too.

One evening the girls and their father were on their way to a party at a great London house. Flo was wearing her favorite dress. It was made of corn-colored silk with flounces of black lace. She carried a bouquet of yellow roses sent to her by an admiring young man.

The carriage stopped before an imposing

[*91*]

doorway. As Flo stepped out of the carriage she saw that a small crowd had collected on the sidewalk to watch the guests arriving for the party. A misty rain had begun to fall. The wind, blowing up from the river, was chilly.

Flo reached to draw her warm cloak about her. As her hand closed on the soft velvet and fur, she saw that the group of people on the side-walk were watching her.

They shivered in that same wind, but they

had no warm cloaks to draw about them. Among them she saw a few thin-faced, wide-eyed children. They stood barefoot on the hard wet pavement, and their feet were blue with cold.

A stout, richly dressed gentleman came pushing through them. He hurried up the steps to the reception. "What dirty beggars!" Flo heard him say. "They shouldn't be allowed to stare so at their betters!"

A great rush of feeling swept through Flo. *"Those are my brothers and my sisters!"* a voice seemed to cry within her.

She followed Parthe up the steps and through the open doorway. She walked almost in a daze. A servant in livery took her cloak. She heard the orchestra playing the latest waltz. The house blazed with candles, and the jewels of the guests sparkled.

How different this scene was from the one just outside the door! Suddenly it seemed more than Flo could bear. She remembered her visit to Mrs. Hodge's poor cottage, six years

[*94*]

Among them she saw thin-faced, wide-eyed children

before. She remembered, too, the Voice that had seemed to call her to God's service. "And I've done nothing at all!" she confessed to herself sadly. "I've thought only of the good times I was having at parties and balls. But from now on I will really and truly try to do God's work and help His poor."

CHAPTER TEN

Disappointment and New Hope

SOON after this, the Nightingales moved back to Embley Park to spend the fall and winter. Flo went to see her friend, the Vicar's wife.

"Where can I find the poorest and most wretched people in the parish?" she asked. "I want to help them."

"Come with me to the Pauper's Hospital," Mrs. Giffard said.

The next morning she and Flo drove to the ancient stone building where penniless sick people were cared for. It was dark and damp inside. A terrible odor met Flo's nostrils as soon as she entered the door. It grew worse as they walked up the stairs to the sick wards.

[97]

It grew worse as they walked upstairs

"The hospital smell!" the Vicar's wife said, holding her handkerchief to her nose. "It's dreadful, isn't it? But I suppose the poor creatures become used to it."

"The fever is bad this year, and the wards are crowded," the matron in charge told them.

The beds stood so close together that Flo and Mrs. Giffard could barely pass between them.

"Don't let your skirts touch the beds," the matron said in warning.

"Why not?" Flo asked.

"Lice, my dear young lady!" the matron said shortly.

The floor felt damp and slimy under their feet. The one narrow window was tightly closed. Flo saw that it had been nailed shut.

"Shouldn't there be more fresh air?" she suggested.

"Oh no! That might chill the poor creatures," the matron explained.

A nurse carrying a tray passed them. She was a stout, red-faced woman. Her dress and apron were soiled and spotted. Her hair straggled untidily about her face. The smell of liquor hung in the air around her.

"That was Mrs. Wyatt, my best nurse," the matron said. "She's strong and willing, and the patients all like her cheerful manner."

"But—" the Vicar's wife said. "But she's been drinking, Matron!"

The matron shrugged her shoulders. "I suppose so. But so do all the nurses I've ever known. If they didn't drink, or if they had good characters, they wouldn't have to work in hospitals at all. They could find other positions."

Flo looked at the faces that stared up from the lines of beds. So many suffering human beings who needed help! Surely this was the place for her to begin the work she had vowed to do.

As they drove home, Flo's eyes were shining. "I'll come here regularly until I get acquainted with the patients and learn their special needs," she said. "Then I'll know how best to help them."

Mrs. Giffard did not answer. She had thought that the sight of the hospital would discourage the eager girl. Now she was worried. Would Mrs. Nightingale allow her daughter to do the work she planned? She shook her head doubtfully.

As soon as she reached home Flo hurried to find her mother. Mrs. Nightingale sat in her room before her mirror. Clémence was brushing her long, dark brown hair.

Flo told her mother where she had been. But before she had a chance to explain her plan, Mrs. Nightingale gave an exclamation of horror.

"The Pauper's Hospital? Mrs. Giffard took you *there?*" she cried. "I wonder at her! Never, never go there again. The place reeks with fever. I only hope you haven't caught it yourself!"

When she saw how displeased her mother was, Flo did not dare even to mention her plan. Sadly she gave it up. "I'll find some other way to keep my promise," she told herself.

But it was very difficult for Flo to change her way of living. She was kept too busy in her mother's world of fashionable society and her father's world of books. As time passed she grew restless and discouraged.

Whenever she could, she visited the poor people in the village and helped them in many ways. But Parthe objected even to that.

"Flo is getting to be so queer," she complained to her parents. "She makes it very hard for me. I had to explain again today that Flo couldn't come to a garden party because she was reading aloud to some sick old man. Lady Maude wasn't pleased at all!"

Then something happened which gave Flo's thoughts a new turn. Her young cousin, Shore Smith, who was now fourteen, came to stay with the Nightingales. A bad attack of the measles had left him thin and with a painful cough.

As soon as he arrived Flo tucked him into bed in a sunny, airy room overlooking the garden. She mixed flour and mustard together with water and spread the mixture on a piece of old linen. Then she put the mustard plaster on his chest.

He sighed with relief as the warmth eased

the deep soreness. Then Flo brought him a cool, sweet, creamy eggnog flavored with nutmeg.

"I'll soon have you brown and sturdy," she told him. "We'll go tramping over the Downs again. And near the house, in a place you'll never guess, there's a nuthatch's nest."

"Truly?" His face was brighter already.

Flo adjusted the shade of the window so that the light did not shine in his eyes. "Yes, truly. But I shan't tell you where it is. I'll take you there, but you'll have to find it yourself," she said, smiling.

"You're such a good nurse, Flo," he said. "When old Emmons puts a mustard plaster on me it's either so strong that it burns or else it's cold and clammy. Have you studied a lot of big books about how to nurse, Flo?"

She shook her head. "No, there aren't any books to teach nursing, Shore," she said.

"But why not?" Shore asked curiously. "There ought to be a school where people could learn. Isn't it important to know the best ways of caring for sick people?"

[*103*]

"It is, very important," Flo told him. "And I think that something should be done about it, don't you?"

"Yes," Shore said. Then he gave a great yawn. "I'm sleepy. But I'm beginning to figure out where that nuthatch's nest must be. I'll wager I find it the first thing in the morning."

"We'll see," Flo said. She closed his door softly. But Shore's last question had given her an idea. Already she was trying to make a plan for carrying it out.

One evening, some time later, a doctor named Fowler, and his wife were guests at Embley Park. Dr. Fowler was the head of the Salisbury Infirmary. Flo knew that he was wise and kind.

After dinner Florence turned to speak to him. "Dr. Fowler," she said, "I'd like to ask help from you. I've been caring for sick people in my family and in the village. But I find that I do not know the best methods of nursing, and I'd like to learn them.

"Would you allow me to work in your hospital for about three months?" she continued.

[104]

"I would come and work as an ordinary nurse just to learn the skill that I need."

"Florence!" Mrs. Nightingale fairly shrieked her name. "Florence. *You*, a hospital nurse? What a dreadful way to joke!"

Florence looked around the room. Every face was surprised and shocked.

"I'm not joking, Mama," Flo said earnestly.

Mrs. Nightingale sank back in her chair. "Dr. Fowler, tell this foolish, ignorant girl how unsuitable such a thing would be," she begged.

"Really, Miss Flo," the doctor began. "Really, it's as your dear mother says, believe me. The work is most unpleasant and difficult. But that is not the worst part. Think of the people you would have to know! Hospital nurses are not the sort of women that a refined young lady should ever meet."

"But—" Flo began.

Her mother interrupted her again. "Not another word! I can bear no more." Her head fell back against the cushions of her chair and she closed her eyes.

Parthe brought her mother's smelling salts.

[*105*]

Dr. Fowler rubbed her wrists. Mr. Nightingale pressed a glass of water to her lips. And Mrs. Fowler fanned her.

Flo turned and fled. In her own room she threw herself face downward on the bed. "Shall I never be allowed to do anything worth doing?" she asked herself, almost in despair.

Flo was deeply disappointed because she could not carry out her plan. But she would not give up hope.

Among the Nightingales' friends was the Ambassador from Prussia, who was named Bunsen. He and his English wife had taken a special liking to Florence. When Flo learned that they, too, were interested in helping the poor, she told them her own hopes and problems. She even told them about her attempt to work in a hospital.

To her surprise, they were not shocked at all. "Have you ever thought of taking nurses' training at Kaiserswerth?" Ambassador Bunsen asked her.

"Kaiserswerth?" Flo repeated.

"Have you never heard of it?" Bunsen asked. "The Institute of Kaiserswerth is on the river Rhine, in Germany."

"It was started by Pastor Fliedner," Madame Bunsen added. "Elizabeth Fry advised and helped him."

"Elizabeth Fry?" Flo repeated. She had heard that name many years earlier when she had been boating with Uncle Oc and Freddy. Her heart began to beat faster.

"Pastor Fliedner began his work by helping freed prisoners to become good citizens again," Bunsen explained. "He opened a refuge for them. Later he added a free school for little children, an orphanage, and then a hospital in which to train volunteer nurses. But it will be better for you to read his own reports. I'll send some of them to you at once," he promised.

Florence could hardly wait until the booklets about Kaiserswerth arrived. She sat up all night reading them.

"That is where I long to be," she said to herself when she had finished. "I *must* go to Kaiserswerth!"

CHAPTER ELEVEN

Kaiserswerth

THE children's ward in the Kaiserswerth Hospital was bright with the summer sun. The bare wooden floors were scrubbed clean and the windowpanes sparkled. The sick children in the rows of plain little beds had had their baths and their breakfasts. Most of them now lay comfortably drowsy and contented.

But not six-year-old Anna Marie. She lay stiff and silent, staring up at the ceiling. Her small hands clutched the coverlet tightly.

In the next bed little Trudi raised herself on her elbow. "Does your tummy hurt, Anna Marie?" she whispered to the younger girl.

Anna Marie's head moved on her pillow.

[*109*]

"No," she answered. Then she pressed her lips tightly together again.

"Then what's the matter? Are you lonesome?"

"Yes," Anna Marie answered with a sob. "I —I want my mother!"

There was a rustle of starched skirts. The new nursing Sister was coming. The new Sister was English, Trudi had learned. She talked German oddly, but her voice was pretty and silvery-soft. Her hands had been smooth and white and soft, too, at first. Now they were getting rough, like the other Sisters' hands, from so much scrubbing and washing.

But it was her face that Trudi liked to look at. Her face was like an angel's in a picture in church. She had a beautiful name, too. Trudi had learned to say it in English. It was Florence Nightingale.

Flo paused beside Trudi's bed. "Aren't you going to have a little nap now, Trudi, like the others?" she asked, smiling.

"Yes, Sister, but Anna Marie can't sleep," Trudi told her. "She's homesick."

"Can I do anything for you, Anna Marie?" Flo asked, bending over the cot. She brushed a strand of flaxen hair off the child's forehead. "Would you like a cool drink?"

Anna Marie's round blue eyes looked sad. She seemed to be holding back tears, but she did not answer.

"Wait. I have an idea," Flo said. She took her handkerchief out of her apron pocket and began to fold and tie knots in it. "There, now!" A funny little puppet figure made of the handkerchief was dancing over Anna Marie's coverlet. "His name is Robin-a-bob-bin, and he likes to see little girls laugh," Flo said.

Anna Marie began to smile. She reached out both hands. "Is it a dolly? Is it for me? I never had a dolly of my own before," she whispered.

"Of course it's for you, darling," Flo said to her.

Anna Marie hugged the little figure close. She drew a deep, quivering sigh and turned on her stomach. Flo drew the covers over her. Almost at once she was asleep.

[*111*]

"Is it a dolly? Is it for me?"

Trudi smiled at Flo. "*I* have a doll," she said. "The Pastor's wife gave all the girls here dolls at Christmastime."

Flo bent and dropped a kiss on the pale little cheek. Trudi looked up into her eyes. "I like you," she said. "You look so happy."

Another nurse entered the ward. "It is time for you to go to lunch, Sister Florence," she said.

Flo went out into the warm August air. As she walked along the path toward the dining hall she was thinking of what Trudi had said. "Does my happiness show so plainly?" she wondered.

It had taken Florence five years to persuade her family to let her come here to Kaiserswerth. At last, unwillingly, they had consented. How long those five years had seemed!

Yet they had not been wasted. Flo had used them to study everything that had been written about hospitals. She had also traveled abroad with her good friends, Mr. and Mrs. Bracebridge, visiting hospitals and asking questions about how they were run.

[*113*]

Now, at Kaiserswerth, she was learning the finest methods of nursing. As she walked along the path to the dining hall in her plain uniform, apron, and cap, she had never felt more contented. She ate her noon dinner of vegetable soup and coarse black bread. Ten minutes were allowed to the student nurses for their meals. Then they must be back at work again.

As Flo was rising from the table, one of the Deaconesses spoke to her. "Go at once to the surgery room, Sister Florence," she said. "You are to watch an operation today."

Florence went obediently, but her heart was beating fast. She had never seen an operation.

"A man had his leg crushed under a cart," one of the students whispered to Flo when she entered the surgery. "They have just brought him in. I think they will have to cut the leg off."

There was no anesthesia to relieve pain or put the patient to sleep. Strong-armed men held the man on the operating table. The surgeon set about his work, heedless of groans and screams.

More than once during the long, dreadful operation Flo thought she was going to faint. But she forced herself to stay to the end. "They are working to save a man's life," she told herself. "And I *must* watch, so that I can learn how to save lives, too."

Later, on that same day, Flo took some boys who had been ill out for a walk. They followed a path along the banks of the Rhine. As usual, the boys were full of questions about Flo's home in faraway England.

"We live most of the time in the country," Flo said. "There are a great many birds around our house. My young cousin and I have tamed some of them to come and eat from our hands."

The boys' eyes brightened. "Tamed them? What kind of birds?" young Erik asked.

"Nuthatches, mostly," Flo explained. "I'll find out the German name for them tomorrow and tell you. And then I have a tiny dwarf owl.

"She came from Greece. I got her while I was traveling there. Some Greek boys found her and sold her to me. I named her Athena, and I carried her all the way home to England in my pocket.

"When she's hungry she calls for her dinner like this," Flo said

"When she's hungry she calls for her dinner like this." Flo put her folded hands against her lips. An owlet's soft hoot rang out strangely above the sound of the water rippling along the river's shore.

"Show me how to do that!" Erik begged.

"And me!" "And me, too!" the other boys cried.

When they returned to the hospital from their walk it seemed as though the boys' ward was suddenly filled by a flock of young and hungry owls!

The work at Kaiserswerth was hard and the discipline was strict. For three months Flo worked and studied. At the end of the term, she took her last examination. And Pastor Fliedner told her that she had passed the nursing course with the highest honors.

Flo left Kaiserswerth in October of 1851. She journeyed up the Rhine River to the city of Cologne. Her mother and Parthe were waiting there for her. Their fine hotel rooms and their fashionable clothes looked strange to Flo after the plain, simple life at Kaiserswerth.

"Well, Flo," her mother exclaimed, as soon as the first greetings were over. "I hope you've had enough of this strange hobby of yours. I trust that you're ready now to come home to the life you were meant for."

"Oh Mama," Flo begged. "Please, *please* try to understand. This is the life I was meant for, the life I *must* lead. I am going next to a hospital in Paris to study. My friends, the Sidney Herberts, visited me while I was at Kaiserswerth. And Liz Herbert is going to help me find a position in a London hospital when I have finished my studies in Paris."

"A position in a hospital?" Mrs. Nightingale cried in horror. "In *London!*"

Parthe burst into tears. "Oh, we shall be disgraced forever!" she wailed. "I can't bear it!"

"If you won't think of yourself, Flo, *do* consider your sister!" her mother said. "She needs you at home. Parthe depends on you so much, Flo. She suffers terribly when you are away."

Flo drew a long breath. "Parthe and I are both grown women now, Mama," she said.

[*118*]

"We must stand on our own feet and make our own decisions."

Her mother argued and Parthe had hysterics. But Flo would not give up her plans. "I'll travel home with you both, now," she stated. "But afterwards I shall go to Paris."

CHAPTER TWELVE

Freedom at Last

MRS. SIDNEY HERBERT kept her promise to find a position for her friend. When Flo returned to London from her Paris studies, she became head of a London hospital for women. It was not large, but Flo now had a chance to use what she had learned at Kaiserswerth and in Paris.

When Flo had been at the hospital for some time, her cousin Hilary called to see her. She was ushered into a pleasant waiting room.

"I'll tell Miss Nightingale that you're here, miss," said a neatly dressed young nurse named Susan Gray.

A few moments later, Flo entered. Hilary had never seen her cousin look more beautiful. Flo's plain black uniform was very becoming to her. A cap of thin white net made her chestnut-colored hair seem brighter than ever.

"You'll never believe where I was when you came, Hilary," Flo said. "Down in the coal cellar, poking about with a stick. I wanted to make sure the dealer didn't send us dust instead of coal, this time!"

"I'd like to see everything in your hospital, Flo," Hilary said. "Do show me around."

Flo led her cousin through the neat waiting room and office to the kitchens and storerooms. Hilary saw cleanliness and order everywhere. Then up the stairs they went, to the rooms where the patients were cared for.

The women patients were of all ages. Each one greeted Flo eagerly as she passed, and she spoke to each one by name.

"You seem to have won their hearts already, Flo," Hilary said.

Flo smiled. "The hospital had been badly managed before I came. It was very much run down when I took it over. I've made a great many changes."

[*121*]

"What changes have you made?" Hilary asked with interest.

"The most important are those that save the nurses unnecessary work," Flo answered. "I have had hot water piped to every floor, for one thing. Now the nurses do not have to carry heavy pitchers and pails up countless stairs every day. With plenty of hot water, things are kept much cleaner.

"I've also installed a new lifting arrangement run by a windlass. It is sometimes called a 'dumb-waiter.' It lifts large containers of food from the kitchen to each floor. Now the nurses do not have to go up and downstairs with heavy trays."

"How very helpful that must be!" Hilary exclaimed. "Your nurses look pleasant and respectable," she added.

Flo nodded. "They are the best I could find," she said. "But some day—" Her gray eyes grew dreamy. "Some day I hope to start a training school for nurses. I learned so much at Kaiserswerth which I'd like to pass on! There are many English girls, I'm sure, who'd like to study nursing if they could find a decent place to learn. Nursing should be a noble profession—not a job for women who can't get anything else to do."

They had paused outside a patient's door. "The girl in here," Flo said in a low voice, "has been a governess. She was taken ill, and she had nowhere to go. Liz Herbert heard of her and sent her to me. She was very sick and nearly died. Now she is well enough to leave, but she is not well enough to go back to work. I have a plan for her. Come in with me while I tell her about it."

They knocked and entered the room. A young girl was sitting in a big chair by the window. Her large dark eyes brightened at sight of Florence.

"Good morning, Alice. This is my cousin, Miss Bonham Carter," Flo said. "How are you this morning?"

"Much better," Alice answered, but her thin, pale face looked anxious. "I know I should be leaving here soon, Miss Nightingale. But I don't know yet just where I can go."

"How would you like to go to the seaside?"
Flo asked

"That's what I've come to speak about," Flo said. "How would you like to go to the seaside for a few weeks? I know of a place where you will be well cared for. The sea air will help you to grow strong. And don't worry about money. It's all been arranged."

Tears stood in Alice's eyes. "You are far too good, Miss Nightingale," she said. "How can I ever repay you?"

"By taking care of yourself and getting well," Flo told her. "That's all the reward I want, believe me."

Outside the door again Hilary smiled at her cousin. "You *are* kind, Flo," she said. "You are paying her bills yourself, aren't you?"

"Yes," Flo replied. "Papa has given me money of my own at last. It is a wonderful feeling to be able to spend money as I wish. And I need so very little for myself."

The young nurse, Susan Gray, now appeared again. "Dr. Bowman is here, Miss Nightingale," she announced.

"And I must leave," Hilary said.

The cousins walked down the stairs to-

[*125*]

gether. "Have you seen my mother or Parthe lately?" Flo asked.

Hilary nodded. "They are both well. But they never speak of you, Flo. I'm afraid they still disapprove of your work."

Flo sighed. "I know they do," she said sadly.

Hilary left and Flo hurried to meet Dr. Bowman, who was the chief physician of the hospital. They visited his patients together. When this was over, Dr. Bowman lingered a moment.

"Miss Nightingale," he said, "this hospital of yours is very well run. I am amazed at how well you manage it."

"Thank you, Dr. Bowman," Flo answered. She knew that he was one of the best doctors in London, and it was good to hear his praise.

"King's College Hospital is being remodeled," Dr. Bowman went on. "We mean to make it the finest hospital in London. When it is finished, would you like to be Superintendent of Nurses there?"

Flo caught her breath. She was too surprised to answer for a moment. "Oh, Doctor!" was all she managed to say.

"I can't promise you the position," Dr. Bowman said. "You look so young and pretty! It may be hard for me to persuade the other doctors that you can fill such an important post. But I'll try."

He clapped on his stovepipe hat, wrapped his cloak about him, and went out into the snowy street.

Almost before the door had closed behind him, Flo was beginning to make plans. "King's College Hospital!" she repeated. "There could be no better place for my training school!" Her dreams were coming true more swiftly than she had dared to hope.

Winter passed and spring came, then summer. London grew hot and muggy. Flo thought longingly of the cool, breezy hills around Lea Hurst. "The hospital is running so smoothly. Why not take a holiday?" she thought.

Then an epidemic of a terrible disease called cholera broke out in London. Flo forgot her holiday plans. She offered to work in the hospital where the cholera patients were treated.

She was put in charge of the women patients. The hospital was overcrowded. The sick women were terrified of the dreadful disease. But Flo went about her work quietly and calmly.

She was on her feet from Friday until Sunday afternoon during the first terrible week. But her voice was soft and clear as she gave her orders. Her hands were steady and skillful as she undressed the suffering women, put them into bed, and cared for them.

"Who is that young nurse who is directing the work so well?" a doctor asked.

"That's Miss Nightingale. She's the one Dr. Bowman recommends for the position of Superintendent at King's College Hospital," another answered.

"Well, I shall recommend her also," the first doctor declared.

"And I," another agreed without hesitation.

When the epidemic was over, Dr. Bowman told Flo that the new position would be hers in the fall if she wished it.

"It's a great opportunity for service," Flo said happily.

But suddenly another and far greater opportunity was given to Florence Nightingale.

CHAPTER THIRTEEN

The Great Call

FLORENCE NIGHTINGALE sat in the office of her little hospital. She was reading the *London Times,* and a worried frown drew her brows together.

A war was going on in a place called the Crimea on the Black Sea. A large army of British soldiers had been sent to the Crimea to help France and Turkey fight against Russia. With the army the *London Times* had sent a reporter. Now the reporter had sent back dreadful news.

As she read it, Florence drew in her breath with a gasp of horror.

"What is it, Miss Nightingale?" her assistant, Susan Gray, asked anxiously.

"There has been a terrible battle, Susan," Florence replied, glancing up from the paper. "Thousands of British soldiers have been wounded. They have been sent to the British hospital at Scutari. But no preparations have been made to take care of them.

"There are not enough doctors in the hospital. There are no nurses. And there is not even linen to make bandages. Wounded men are dying every day because there is no one to care for them."

She struck the paper sharply with her hand. "Something must be done," she said. "This is a disgrace to our country. It must be remedied at once!"

"But how?" Susan asked. "What can anyone do?"

"Why, some Englishwomen must go out there to the military hospitals and care for our wounded soldiers," Flo said. Her voice was suddenly firm. "*I* shall go, myself, as soon as I can gather a group of nurses."

"But there have never been women nurses in British army hospitals," Susan cried.

"There will be now," Miss Nightingale replied firmly. And, laying aside her newspaper, she began to make some plans.

Soon she was writing to her good friends, Mr. and Mrs. Sidney Herbert, to tell them that she and a few other nurses were getting ready to sail for Scutari. Since Mr. Herbert was the Secretary of War, she asked his advice about what hospital supplies she should take.

Off went the letter. But even before it reached Mr. Herbert, Flo received a letter from *him*. When she read it, she could hardly believe her eyes.

The Secretary of War had also decided that women nurses should be allowed in army hospitals. He wanted to know if Miss Nightingale would be willing to take forty nurses to Scutari. She was to select and direct the nurses herself. And she could call on the Government for any help she needed.

"There is but one person in England that I know of who would be capable of organizing and superintending such a scheme," wrote Mr. Herbert. And he added that he hoped she would go.

Florence read the letter through again. "This is a great honor," she thought. "No woman has ever been given such responsibility by the Army before." She knew, however, that she was ready for the work, and that she could do it.

Mrs. Herbert's house in London was a strange sight during the next few days. For Florence Nightingale was using it as her headquarters. It was crowded with busy, bustling people.

In the drawing room Liz Herbert was interviewing the nurses who wanted to go on the expedition. Parthe Nightingale was there too, helping her. To Flo's joy, her sister had offered to aid in the preparations as soon as she heard the news.

In the dining room, dressmakers were cutting, sewing, and fitting the uniforms Miss Nightingale had designed for her nurses. Her friends, the Bracebridges, were going to Scutari with her, and Mrs. Bracebridge had charge of this work.

Tradesmen came and went, bringing parcels and boxes. Messengers brought letters and took away answers.

In the middle of all the excitement and confusion, Flo sat at a desk checking lists, giving orders, and answering questions.

"How can you be so calm, Flo?" Liz exclaimed, wiping her own damp forehead.

Flo smiled, but she did not answer. "I have been preparing for this work all my life," she thought.

The door opened and Mr. Bracebridge strode in. "I have arranged for passage to France, and bought the train tickets from Paris to Marseilles," he said. "There we will board the English steamer *Vectis*."

[*134*]

"Good!" Flo said. "Then I can buy whatever hospital supplies I plan to take, in Marseilles. That will save having to transport them across France."

Mr. Bracebridge paused. "I stopped in at the office of the Army Medical Service to ask what they would advise you to take," he said. "They told me that there is nothing needed at the Scutari hospitals now. They say that the reports in the *London Times* were not true. They have plenty of supplies at Scutari."

"Perhaps," Flo said doubtfully. "But I think that I shall purchase supplies in Marseilles, just the same. Those reports in the *Times* sounded only too true, to me."

Liz Herbert came hurrying up with a sheaf of papers for Flo to sign. "What is that strange vehicle standing before the door, Mr. Bracebridge?" she asked. "Did you arrive in it?"

"That, my dear young lady, is one of the newfangled hansom cabs," Mr. Bracebridge answered, smiling. "All London is talking about them. The thing fairly flies through the streets. I made at least ten miles an hour on my last errand!"

"That is one of the newfangled hansom cabs,"
Mr. Bracebridge said

"Ten miles an hour!" Liz cried in wonder. "Well, we need all the minutes you can save, that's sure."

"You and Selina have been of great help to me, Mr. Bracebridge," Flo said earnestly. "I'm so thankful that you are coming out to Scutari with us!"

"We're only too glad to be useful," Mr. Bracebridge said. "I believe that everyone in England would help you if he could. You're fast becoming a national heroine, Florence. The British people are furious because their wounded men are being neglected in Scutari. They can't do enough for someone who is going there to help them."

Flo had set Saturday, October 21, as the day of departure. But no one else would believe that they could be ready so soon. "Why, that will be less than a week after you received Mr. Herbert's letter!" Selina Bracebridge had exclaimed.

But, Saturday, nevertheless, the whole group left London, bound for France. Cheering crowds came to the ship to see them off.

[137]

Most precious to Flo, however, was the loving letter her mother had sent to her, and the memory of Parthe's proud and happy face. "That is all that I lacked," she thought. "With the love and understanding of my own family, I can face anything."

So Florence Nightingale set sail on her great adventure. She carried with her the deep prayers and gratitude of the British people. She would need all their prayers, and she would deserve all their gratitude for the work she was to do.

CHAPTER FOURTEEN

A Strange Welcome

IT WAS a dismal November morning. Rain was falling. The steamer *Vectis* was anchored at last off Scutari. Florence leaned on the ship's rail and peered through the thick mist. She could see some large buildings on the hills above the shore. "Is that the hospital?" she wondered.

A rowboat came alongside the *Vectis*. A young army officer climbed briskly up the ladder. "I present the compliments of our general, Lord Raglan," he said, saluting. "He welcomes you, Miss Nightingale, on behalf of the whole Army."

"Thank you, Captain," Florence answered. "And please thank Lord Raglan for me. I hope

[*139*]

we shall deserve his welcome. Tell me, what's the news of the war?"

The officer's face darkened. "Bad news, ma'am," he said. "There has been another battle at Balaclava. Our brave Light Brigade charged, but it was almost wiped out. The wounded will soon be under your care."

"We shall be ready for them, Captain," Florence promised.

It was time for the party to land. Scutari had no pier. The nurses had to climb down rope ladders from the ship to small rowboats. They were drenched with spray and rain when at last they stood on the beach.

A medical officer was there to meet them. His manner was polite, but cold. "Please follow me," he said. "I will show you to your quarters."

Before them rose a steep, muddy slope. No road, but only a winding track, led up from the shore. The nurses followed him, toiling up through the slippery mud in their long, wet skirts.

The officer pointed to an enormous yellow

The officer pointed to an enormous yellow building

building on the hillside. "Your quarters are there, in what we call the Barrack Hospital," he said. "It was given to us by the Turks when our own general hospital filled up with cholera cases. It used to be a Turkish barracks."

"Cholera!" one of the nurses exclaimed in alarm.

Flo silenced her with a look. But not before she had seen a scornful smile on the officer's face.

As they approached, the Barrack Hospital seemed to grow more and more enormous. There were towers at each of its corners. About it was a sea of mud. The enclosed courtyard was like a pond, and was littered with refuse.

The guide led the nurses up a stone stairway in one of the towers. "Here are your quarters, ma'am," he announced to Miss Nightingale. "You are to cook, eat, and sleep here." Then he was gone.

"Well, let's see what we have," Florence said.

The nurses looked around and what they saw filled them with dismay. There were five small rooms to hold forty-four people. The rooms were dirty and littered. Rats scuttled across the floor and cockroaches ran up the damp walls.

"A lively committee of welcome!" Flo said. Some of the nurses were able to smile faintly in answer.

"There is no furniture! There are not even beds!" Mrs. Bracebridge exclaimed.

Raised wooden platforms ran around the walls of some of the rooms. "Those could serve for beds," Mr. Bracebridge suggested.

But there was no bedding. There was no food, no fuel, and no stoves. The women were cold and hungry, and night was coming on. For a moment even Florence Nightingale was dismayed and silent.

"We must provide for ourselves," she said, rallying her courage. "Begin to unpack our things. I'll see what I can find."

While the nurses unpacked the clothing and supplies, Florence Nightingale went down the stairs to the hospital. She returned later with a pailful of tea which was all that she had been able to find for supper. There was no sugar nor milk, but at least the tea was strong and hot. She poured it out into tin basins which she had brought upstairs also.

While the nurses drank their tea awkwardly from the shallow basins, Flo told them what she had learned.

"Conditions here in this hospital are worse, far worse, than the *Times* reported," she said. "When I saw what the sick and wounded men are having to endure, I was ashamed to complain of our quarters here.

"There are not nearly enough beds for the patients. Many wounded men are lying on the floors. They are in the same stiff, blood-soaked clothes in which they fell on the battlefield. There are no clean hospital shirts for them to wear. There are not even any sheets."

The nurses exclaimed in horror. "But they told us in England that everything had been provided, now," Nurse Anna protested.

"I know," Florence agreed. "Someone has managed things badly. But I haven't told you everything yet. The sewers under this build-

[*144*]

ing are all clogged up. The lavatories in the wards are useless. The whole place is filthy from top to bottom.

"But there are no brooms nor scrubbing brushes," she continued grimly. "There is no laundry. The kitchen has no kettles nor saucepans, only huge copper boilers. The fuel for them is green wood. And the food served to sick and wounded men is half-raw meat and half-cooked pease porridge!"

Nurse Bertha could hold in her indignation no longer. "But that is disgraceful!" she cried.

"Let's waste no more time talking," stout, motherly Nurse Lawfield cried. "I'll clean one ward, tonight, even if I have to use my own petticoat for a mop!"

She was interrupted by a scream from one of the women, who pointed upward. An enormous, gray-whiskered rat sat on a rafter above their heads. Its small eyes gleamed red in the twilight and it showed long, yellow fangs in an angry snarl.

The others were too frightened to move, but Florence swiftly slipped off her shoe.

Florence swiftly slipped off her shoe

"I shouldn't miss. I've had too much practice throwing balls for my cousin Shore to bat," she declared. And she hurled the shoe with all her force.

The shoe struck the rat and knocked it to the floor. Mr. Bracebridge soon disposed of it. For a moment this raised the nurses' spirits. "We should give Miss Nightingale a military decoration for courage," Nurse Bertha suggested. "A medal, picturing a rat with a shoe striking it."

Several of the nurses laughed. But Miss Nightingale had more bad news for them.

"The doctors in the hospital don't want us here," she said. "Dr. Hall, their chief, was very angry at the *Times* reports, because they criticized his work. He has ordered his doctors to have nothing to do with us."

"But the Government sent us!" Nurse Roberts exclaimed. "They *can't* keep us from doing the work we were sent here to do!"

Florence shook her head. "There is a rule that no nurse may even enter a ward, unless requested to do so by the doctor who is in charge," she told them.

[*147*]

"Just let anyone try to keep *me* from doing my duty by those poor soldiers!" Mrs. Lawfield cried. "I'll soon show them!"

Flo smiled, but she shook her head again. "No, we must not be angry. We must be patient and tactful," she said. "We must win over the doctors if we hope to help the patients. I told Lord Raglan's aide that we would be ready for the wounded when they arrived. I mean to keep my word. Just how we shall manage I don't know yet. But I shall find a way."

CHAPTER FIFTEEN

"A Lady with a Lamp"

FLORENCE NIGHTINGALE'S party slept very little that night. They were all cold and hungry. Fleas bit them, the wooden benches were hard, and rats ran about the room all night.

Florence rose in the early dawn and looked out at the bright sky. Across the shining water she could see the domes and minarets of Constantinople. It was one of the most beautiful views in all the world. But she gave it only a brief glance.

Already she had made her plans. "We will set up the portable stoves in here which we brought from Marseilles," she told her nurses.

"We will make hot, nourishing drinks and have them ready for the wounded when they are brought here from the ships. Surely no doctor will refuse that help for his patients at a time like this."

The stretchers, loaded with sick and wounded soldiers, soon began to pour into the hospital. Miss Nightingale and her nurses stood waiting at the entrance to each ward.

"May we serve these hot drinks to your patients?" Miss Nightingale asked respectfully of each doctor in turn. No one refused, as she had foreseen. And before the week was over, her nurses were working in the wards, cleaning, dressing wounds, and caring for the sick.

Meanwhile more and more men arrived from the battlefields. Besides the wounded, there were men suffering from cold and frostbite. Others were sick with fever and cholera. The hospital was swamped with cases, and confusion grew. Medicines, bandages, food—everything seemed to be lacking.

The chief supply officer sat in his office. Papers were stacked high on his desk and on the floor around him. There was so much to be done that he had almost given up trying to do anything.

Suddenly he noticed a young woman in black standing in his doorway. "Miss Nightingale!" he exclaimed.

Florence Nightingale went straight to the point. "Before we left England, the Government told us that they had sent all the equipment and supplies the hospitals needed. If it was sent, why hasn't it reached the wards?"

The supply officer shrugged his shoulders. "That's the question," he said. "Some of it was sent to the wrong port. Some has been lost or stolen. Some is in the storehouse, here."

"Here?" Florence said. "If it is here, why isn't it taken out and used?"

The officer looked uncomfortable. "There are papers to be signed, and rules. All these things take time," he said. He felt his face growing red under Miss Nightingale's bright and steady stare.

"And in the meantime, men are dying!" she said. "If the Army cannot find ways to provide for its soldiers, I shall do it. Please tell your doctors that when they need something which they cannot get immediately from you, to come to me.

"I have some supplies already. I shall buy whatever else is needed at the markets in Constantinople. The English people have raised a large sum of money for me to use in my work. And I can think of no better way to spend it."

"But—" the officer stammered, "that is quite contrary to the rules—"

"Then the rules must be changed," Florence Nightingale told him. She turned and went back to her quarters.

The officer looked after the graceful black-clad figure, and shook his head. "Poor foolish young lady!" he thought. "She'll never do anything that way. She's trying to change the British Army!"

But he was wrong. Before the month was over Florence Nightingale was supplying the whole hospital with many things.

"I am a dealer in socks, shirts, knives and forks, wooden spoons, tin baths, tables and forms, cabbages and carrots, operating tables, towels and soap, combs, lice powder, scissors, bed pans, and pillows," she wrote in one of her long daily reports to Sidney Herbert.

Next, Florence started a laundry. She hired a house in Scutari, and had boilers set up in it. Then she engaged women from the town to work there. Soon there were clean hospital shirts and sheets for the patients.

The commander of the army—Lord Raglan —sent word that five hundred more wounded men were being sent down from the fighting front to the Scutari hospitals.

"But there's no space left even on the floor!" exclaimed the officer in charge of the hospitals, when he heard this news.

"A whole wing of the Barrack Hospital is not in use," Florence said quietly. "I'm told it was destroyed by fire. Why not repair it?"

The officer shook his head. "That fire happened before we took this place over," he explained. "I have no right to have repairs made there. I'd have to get permission from the War Office in London."

"I shall have it done myself then," said Florence Nightingale. She hired workmen, bought lumber and supplies, and drew up plans. By the time the ships arrived bringing the wounded, the new wing was ready for them.

But still the disasters grew. The British Army had failed to supply its troops with warm clothing or proper food. Winter came. The men suffered cruelly in the icy trenches from hunger and cold. The cholera increased. More than half the Army lay wounded and sick. The Nightingale nurses worked from before dawn to after dark with quiet heroism.

But night did not bring an end to Florence Nightingale's labors.

One night a young transport sailor named

William lay restless and wakeful in his cot. It was almost midnight. The great echoing wards of the Barrack Hospital were dark. The only sound was the slow step of the sentry pacing the stone floor.

William's throat burned with thirst. The pain of his shattered leg seemed more than he could bear. Worst of all was the fear growing in his heart.

"Tomorrow we'll operate," the surgeon had said.

"What does that mean?" William wondered. "Will they cut my leg off? I think I'd rather die, here and now!"

Suddenly he noticed shadows sliding along the ceiling. A light was moving, far down the ward. A whispered murmur passed from man to man. "It's *Her!* It's Miss Nightingale," they said.

She came as quietly as a shadow. When she reached William's cot she set the lantern down and bent over him. Her cool hand touched his forehead. "You're hot and thirsty, William. Here's a drink for you."

[*155*]

Her arm steadied him while he gulped the water. "There, is that better?" she asked. In the lantern light her face was pale, but as kind and gentle as his own mother's.

"Miss Nightingale," William said hoarsely. "Are they going to cut off my leg tomorrow?"

Florence Nightingale's face was grave. "I don't know, William," she said. "But I promise you that I shall be there with you all the time. If they can save your leg, they will, you may be sure of that. And will you promise me something?"

"What do you mean, ma'am?" he asked doubtfully.

"Promise me that you will bear whatever they decide like the brave British sailor that you are," she asked.

He could not refuse *Her*. "Yes, I'll promise," he said.

She smiled. "Now try to sleep." She touched his eyelids and he closed them. But when she moved on, he raised his head and watched the light of her lantern flickering down the long room. She spoke to a soldier here, and smiled at another there. William saw a brawny fellow turn his head and kiss her shadow as it lay for a moment on his pillow.

"She seems to know, somehow, whenever a fellow is a bit low, and she comes to cheer him up," the man next to William said. "She's an angel, and no mistake."

William turned over on his side. He could still feel the touch of her fingers on his eyelids. And what Florence Nightingale did for him that night she did for hundreds, yes, thousands of other men during that terrible and tragic winter.

CHAPTER SIXTEEN

Tommy's Voyage

Howard are you this morning, Tommy?"

The young drummer boy looked up. Miss Nightingale, the Lady-in-Chief herself, was visiting the wards. He sat up straight in his bed and saluted. "I'm fine, ma'am," he answered.

Miss Nightingale smiled. Tommy's cheeks were beginning now to fill out and to show some color. He had been brought in so ill with Crimean fever that no one had expected him to live. Florence Nightingale had refused to give up hope, and she had nursed him herself. She had pulled him through, somehow, as she had done with so many others.

"You look so well that I think we'll get you out of bed for a while," she told him. "Let's see

[*159*]

how your legs will work. Mrs. Roberts and I
will help you."

"I don't need any help!" Tommy boasted.
He slid off the bed and stood up suddenly.

To his astonishment his knees bent under
him. If Miss Nightingale hadn't been there to
catch him, he would have fallen to the floor.

"What's the matter with my feet?" he asked,
looking down at them. "They feel all prickly."

Miss Nightingale was laughing. "That's the
way it always is after a long illness, Tommy,"
she said.

The two nurses helped him to walk up and

down the ward a few times. When he lay down on his bed again he gave a sigh of relief. He was very tired. But the next day he was stronger, and by the end of two weeks he was as lively as a cricket.

"I'm going to put that energy of yours to work, Tommy," Miss Nightingale told him. "I need someone to run errands and carry messages for me. Would you like the job?"

The boy stood stiff and straight as a ramrod, and saluted. "You saved my life, Miss Nightingale," he said. "I'm your man. I'll be glad to forsake my drums and my army career to serve you, ma'am."

From that moment Tommy was Florence Nightingale's devoted helper. He ran her errands. He escorted her when she went from one section of the hospital to another. He took charge of her cape and umbrella in wet weather. And he kept the lantern filled and polished which she carried at night.

Winter passed, and warm spring winds blew across the trampled mud of Scutari. Miss Nightingale's letters and reports to Sidney

Herbert brought some action at last. A group of sanitary engineers arrived from England. They soon cleaned out the sewers under the Barrack Hospital. At once the cases of fever and cholera grew less. The wounded men recovered far faster, now that the air they breathed and the water they drank were clean and pure.

Tommy heard Mr. Bracebridge and Miss Nightingale talking together one morning. "Yes, these hospitals are running smoothly," Florence Nightingale said. "I think I can safely leave them for a while. I want to inspect the front-line hospitals in the Crimea. Some new nurses have been sent from England and put to work there. I've learned that Dr. Hall is making things difficult for them."

She turned and saw Tommy. His eyes were round and pleading. "May I go with you, ma'am?" he begged.

"Of course, Tommy," she told him. "I couldn't get on without you."

Several days later Florence Nightingale set sail on the steamer *Robert Lowe* for Balaclava in the Crimea. Nurse Roberts, three other nurses, two cooks, Mr. Bracebridge, and Tommy went with her.

The *Robert Lowe* arrived at Balaclava on May 5, 1855. When word spread that the Lady-in-Chief was aboard, the troops crowded to the waterside to shout and cheer.

"Before I inspect the hospitals, I should like to visit the front-line trenches," Florence Nightingale said.

A horse with a sidesaddle was brought for her. Tommy thought that he had never seen anything so beautiful as his beloved Miss Nightingale mounted on the spirited little mare. She rode off surrounded by officers in brilliant uniforms. "She's like a queen," he thought.

She returned to the ship that night with her arms full of wild lilies and orchids. They had been picked on the heights of Balaclava and presented to her by the soldiers. "I could not bring them all," she told Tommy. "But I took a few from each man."

She went out to inspect the hospitals the

next day. This time Tommy went with her, walking behind her up and down the endless wards. Even he could see how dirty and disorderly they were.

The chief medical officer, Dr. John Hall, walked beside her. His replies to her quiet,

but searching, questions were haughty and almost rude. Tommy saw Mr. Bracebridge grow red with anger. Mrs. Roberts bit her lip as though to hold back sharp words. Miss Nightingale's face remained calm and serene. Her clear, soft voice never changed.

But when she returned to the ship she lay down at once on the bunk in her cabin. "Dr. Hall can't forgive me for coming out here and disturbing his reign," she said. "He's jealous of the improvements we've made in our hospitals." She added, with a sigh, "I'm very tired, Tommy. So *very* tired."

The next morning she could not get up. Mrs. Roberts called in a doctor. "It's the Crimean fever," he reported. "She is very ill. She must be moved to a hospital on shore."

Four soldiers carried Miss Nightingale, on a stretcher, from the shore up to the hospital on the heights. They moved between lines of silent, anxious men. Mrs. Roberts and the doctor walked beside the stretcher.

Behind them all came Tommy, crying bitterly. "I want to do something to help her," he sobbed. "But they say I'm not strong enough to carry the stretcher."

There were tears on older faces than Tommy's as the procession passed. The soldiers knew how swiftly and terribly the fever struck. They had seen their comrades die of it by the thousands. Was the Lady-in-Chief to die, too?

The news of her illness spread fast. When it reached Scutari, men turned their faces to the wall and wept.

For a while Miss Nightingale was very near

*There were tears on older faces than Tommy's
as the procession passed*

to death. During that time, Tommy never left his place beside the door of the hospital hut where she lay. Mrs. Roberts tried to give him courage. "Everyone is thinking of her," she said. "They are having special church services all over England to pray for her recovery. So many heartfelt prayers *must* make a difference. You'll see."

At last the crisis of the fever came and passed. "She has crossed the danger line," the doctors reported. "She will recover."

That evening a horseman wrapped in a dark cloak rode up to the door of Miss Nightingale's hut. Tommy sprang to his feet as the man dismounted and knocked. Mrs. Roberts appeared in the doorway. "Hush!" she whispered. "Don't make such a noise."

"Is this where Miss Nightingale is lodged?" the stranger asked.

"Yes," Mrs. Roberts answered. "But she cannot see any visitors, my man. Who are you?"

"Only a soldier, but I have ridden a long way. My name is Raglan."

[*168*]

"Oh, Mrs. Roberts, it's the commander—
Lord Raglan!" Tommy cried.

"Well—" Mrs. Roberts said, hesitating.

Miss Nightingale's voice, weak but clear,
came from inside the hut. "Ask Lord Raglan
to come in," she said.

He entered and sat beside her narrow cot. "I
had orders from Queen Victoria to come and
see for myself how you are," he said. "Her
Majesty wants me to telegraph to her tonight
about you. And never was I happier, for I have
good news to send."

Florence Nightingale's recovery was slow.
The doctors said that she was worn out with
all her months of hard work. They advised her
to go home to England and rest.

"No. There is still too much to do here," she
protested. Nothing would make her change
her mind. "So long as there are sick and
wounded to be cared for, I shall remain also,"
she stated.

CHAPTER SEVENTEEN

"I Can Never Forget!"

FLORENCE NIGHTINGALE now was beloved by all the people of England. The poor people, especially, thought of her almost as a saint. Their sons and brothers and husbands in the Army had sent letters home. The letters had been full of stories of Miss Nightingale's courage and devotion.

There was hardly a city tenement or a country cottage that did not have her picture on the wall, or her statue on its mantelpiece. During her illness, people throughout England had prayed for her recovery. When word came that she would get well, strangers had stopped each other on the streets to share the good news.

[*170*]

On November 29, 1855, a great public meeting was held in London. Royal dukes, statesmen, and members of Parliament all made speeches praising Florence Nightingale and her nurses. Other meetings were held in other towns and cities. Money was collected to buy a beautiful gift for Miss Nightingale.

But so much money came pouring in that it was used to start a "Nightingale Fund." This fund was to be used in any way that Miss Nightingale wished. In addition to all this, the Queen sent Florence Nightingale a beautiful jeweled brooch, which had been made especially for her.

At last the bitter Crimean War ended.

When the last soldier had left the hospitals, Florence Nightingale, too, left Scutari for England. The Queen wished to send a battleship to bring her home. Regiments of soldiers asked to be allowed to meet her at the dock with flags flying and bands playing. Cities and towns wanted to give great public receptions in her honor.

But she refused it all. "The gratitude of England should go to the soldiers who fought for her," she declared, "not to me."

Florence traveled quietly home across Europe. She had sent what she called her "spoils of war" home before her. These were William, the sailor boy, whose leg had been cut off ten months earlier in the Scutari hospital, a little Russian orphan named Peter, and a big, rough-coated puppy, and a kitten.

Tommy was already in England. But he had promised to pay Miss Nightingale a long visit as soon as she returned.

Florence Nightingale did not use her own name on her journey. She landed in England unnoticed and went to Lea Hurst alone by train. Her family did not know that she was coming until the puppy began to bark excitedly. They looked out and saw Florence walking alone up the driveway.

She would not allow them to tell people that she had returned. "I am so tired," she said. "I cannot see anyone for a while. And as soon as I am rested, I have work to do. I must plan how best to do it."

But she could not rest. Her mind was filled with pictures of the terrible things she had seen. She paced the floor at night, unable to sleep. Her shadow, moving along the wall, reminded her of the wards at Scutari.

"I can *never* forget!" she thought. "And I

shall make sure that England does not forget those heroic soldiers, either."

She had improved conditions in army hospitals near the battlefield. Now she wanted to improve conditions in all the army hospitals in England. But her good friend, Sidney Herbert, was no longer the Secretary of War. And Lord Panmure, who had taken his place, hated change. He would not even talk with Flo about the work she wished to do.

Poor Florence Nightingale was in despair. Her despair turned to joy, however, when she received a very special invitation. Queen Victoria asked her to call on her at the castle of Balmoral in Scotland. The Queen wished to hear all about her work at Scutari.

The September air was clear and bright when Miss Nightingale traveled northward to Scotland. The rugged hills and deep glens of the Highlands were very beautiful. Purple heather covered the mountainsides. The valleys were rich and green, and the lakes and streams sparkled in the sun.

Balmoral Castle stood high on a hill overlooking the river Dee. As Miss Nightingale's carriage stopped at the great doorway, her heart beat rapidly. A servant in Highland kilts came down the steps to meet her.

She was ushered into the great hall. Almost at once, a lady in waiting came hurrying in to take her to Queen Victoria.

Now, once again Florence Nightingale curtsied before her Queen. The years had changed Victoria from a slim young girl to a plump wife and mother. But her eyes were still blue and friendly.

Miss Nightingale was introduced to the Prince Consort, Victoria's tall, serious husband. Then, for two hours, she talked with them about her work at Scutari. She told them all about the terrible conditions there. They listened with the greatest interest. Both asked many questions.

When the interview was over, the Queen made arrangements for another meeting and then another. She took Miss Nightingale driving alone with her in her pony carriage, and for long walks in the autumn woods.

For two hours, she talked with them about Scutari

Queen Victoria was shocked by the stories of how the soldiers had suffered because they had not had proper care. She promised that she would do everything in her power to see that army hospitals were made better. But even the

Queen could do nothing without permission from her Government. So she sent for Lord Panmure.

The Secretary of War did not wish any changes made in his army hospitals. Unwillingly he went to the castle to talk with Florence Nightingale. For some reason he had expected her to be a large, loud-voiced, bossy

[*177*]

creature. He saw, instead, a woman who was slim and graceful and still young. Her face was serene and lovely and her voice silvery-soft. What was more, she wanted nothing, and would accept nothing, for herself.

Miss Nightingale won him over completely. When he heard what she wanted to do he promised her his help.

Florence Nightingale stayed in the Highlands for a month. Before she left, the Queen and Lord Panmure had promised that a group of important men would be organized to improve conditions in army hospitals and in the soldiers' barracks also.

Miss Nightingale herself was to select these men and tell them what to do. She knew that all this would take time and work and patience. But by now she also knew her own power.

"I *shall* succeed because I *must*," she said to herself as she set out for home.

And she did succeed, although it took her years to do so. It was not easy to change the methods of the British Army. There were

[178]

many times when she was discouraged. Her illness in the Crimea had left her weak and tired. She often had to work lying on a couch, but she never stopped working.

"Rest a little, Flo. Do rest," her mother or Parthe would beg. But Florence had little time for rest. There were too many things which she wanted to do.

Not only did she work to improve conditions in the army hospitals and barracks. She also improved conditions in civilian hospitals. News of what she was doing in England spread throughout the world. The King of Portugal, the Queen of Holland, the Crown Prince of Prussia, the Government of India, and the Government of the United States all sent to her for advice about hospitals in their different countries.

And in 1872 a man from Switzerland spoke before a large audience in London. His name was Henri Dunant, and he had started an organization called the International Red Cross.

"Though I am known as the founder of the Red Cross," he said, "it is to an Englishwoman that all honor is due. What inspired me was the work of Miss Florence Nightingale in the Crimea."

Meanwhile Florence Nightingale had used the money in the "Nightingale Fund" to start an excellent training school for nurses, the first of many.

"Nursing should be a noble profession," she had told her cousin Hilary.

And it *is* a noble profession today because of Florence Nightingale's unceasing work and her shining example.

Signature Books

"Names That Made History"

ENID LaMONTE MEADOWCROFT, *Supervising Editor*

THE STORY OF LOUISA MAY ALCOTT
By Joan Howard.   *Illustrated by Flora Smith*

THE STORY OF JOHN J. AUDUBON
By Joan Howard.   *Illustrated by Federico Castellon*

THE STORY OF CLARA BARTON
By Olive Price.   *Illustrated by Ruth Ives*

THE STORY OF DAN BEARD
By Robert N. Webb.   *Illustrated by Everett Raymond Kinstler*

THE STORY OF BEETHOVEN
By Helen L. Kaufmann.   *Illustrated by Fritz Kredel*

THE STORY OF GOOD QUEEN BESS
By Alida Sims Malkus.   *Illustrated by Douglas Gorsline*

THE STORY OF BUFFALO BILL
By Edmund Collier.   *Illustrated by Nicholas Eggenhofer*

THE STORY OF DANIEL BOONE
By William O. Steele.   *Illustrated by Warren Baumgartner*

THE STORY OF KIT CARSON
By Edmund Collier.   *Illustrated by Nicholas Eggenhofer*

THE STORY OF GEORGE WASHINGTON CARVER
By Arna Bontemps.   *Illustrated by Harper Johnson*

THE STORY OF EDITH CAVELL
By Iris Vinton.   *Illustrated by Gerald McCann*

THE STORY OF WINSTON CHURCHILL
By Alida Sims Malkus.   *Illustrated by Herman B. Vestal*

THE STORY OF CHRISTOPHER COLUMBUS
By Nina Brown Baker.   *Illustrated by David Hendrickson*

THE STORY OF CRAZY HORSE
By Enid LaMonte Meadowcroft.   *Illustrated by William Reusswig*

THE STORY OF DAVY CROCKETT
By Enid LaMonte Meadowcroft.   *Illustrated by C. B. Falls*

THE STORY OF MADAME CURIE
By Alice Thorne.   *Illustrated by Federico Castellon*

THE STORY OF GENERAL CUSTER
By Margaret Leighton.   *Illustrated by Nicholas Eggenhofer*

THE STORY OF AMELIA EARHART
By Adele de Leeuw.   *Illustrated by Harry Beckhoff*

THE STORY OF THOMAS ALVA EDISON
By Enid LaMonte Meadowcroft.   *Illustrated by Harve Stein*

THE STORY OF DWIGHT D. EISENHOWER
By Arthur J. Beckhard.   *Illustrated by Charles Geer*

THE STORY OF LEIF ERICSON
By William O. Steele.   *Illustrated by Pranas Lapé*

THE STORY OF STEPHEN FOSTER
By Esther M. Douty.   *Illustrated by Jo Polseno*

THE STORY OF BENJAMIN FRANKLIN
By Enid LaMonte Meadowcroft.   *Illustrated by Edward A. Wilson*

THE STORY OF GERONIMO
By Jim Kjelgaard.   *Illustrated by Charles Banks Wilson*

THE STORY OF ULYSSES S. GRANT
By Jeannette Covert Nolan.   *Illustrated by Lynd Ward*

THE STORY OF ANDREW JACKSON
By Enid LaMonte Meadowcroft. *Illustrated by David Hendrickson*

THE STORY OF THOMAS JEFFERSON
By Earl Schenck Miers. *Illustrated by Reynold C. Pollak*

THE STORY OF JOAN OF ARC
By Jeannette Covert Nolan. *Illustrated by Pranas Lapé*

THE STORY OF JOHN PAUL JONES
By Iris Vinton. *Illustrated by Edward A. Wilson*

THE STORY OF HELEN KELLER
By Lorena A. Hickok. *Illustrated by Jo Polseno*

THE STORY OF LAFAYETTE
By Hazel Wilson. *Illustrated by Edy Legrand*

THE STORY OF ROBERT E. LEE
By Iris Vinton. *Illustrated by John Alan Maxwell*

THE STORY OF ABRAHAM LINCOLN
By Nina Brown Baker. *Illustrated by Warren Baumgartner*

THE STORY OF MOZART
By Helen L. Kaufmann. *Illustrated by Eric M. Simon*

THE STORY OF FLORENCE NIGHTINGALE
By Margaret Leighton. *Illustrated by Corinne B. Dillon*

THE STORY OF ANNIE OAKLEY
By Edmund Collier. *Illustrated by Leon Gregori*

THE STORY OF LOUIS PASTEUR
By Alida Sims Malkus. *Illustrated by Jo Spier*

THE STORY OF POCAHONTAS
By Shirley Graham. *Illustrated by Mario Cooper*

THE STORY OF MARCO POLO
By Olive Price. *Illustrated by Federico Castellon*

THE STORY OF ELEANOR ROOSEVELT
By Lorena A. Hickok. *Illustrated by William Barss*

THE STORY OF FRANKLIN D. ROOSEVELT
By Lorena A. Hickok. *Illustrated by Leonard Vosburgh*

THE STORY OF THEODORE ROOSEVELT
By Winthrop Neilson. *Illustrated by Edward A. Wilson*

THE STORY OF ROBERT LOUIS STEVENSON
By Joan Howard. *Illustrated by Joe Polseno*

THE STORY OF MARK TWAIN
By Joan Howard. *Illustrated by Donald McKay*

THE STORY OF GEORGE WASHINGTON
By Enid LaMonte Meadowcroft. *Illustrated by Edward A. Wilson*

THE STORY OF MARTHA WASHINGTON
By Jeannette Covert Nolan. *Illustrated by Corinne B. Dillon*

THE STORY OF MAD ANTHONY WAYNE
By Hazel Wilson. *Illustrated by Lawrence Beall Smith*

1 Born in Florence, Italy,
   May 12, 1820

2 Decides to spend her life caring for
   the sick and poor, 1837

3 Presented at Court
   to young Queen Victoria, 1839

4 Studies nursing
   at Kaiserswerth, Germany, 1851

10 Dies in London, England,
   August 13, 1910

8 Becomes ill with
   Crimean fever, but refuses
   to give up her work, 1855

9 Opens the Nightingale School
   for Nurses in England, 1860